CHRONICA BOTANICA

NEW SERIES OF PLANT SCIENCE BOOKS

Consulting Editor, Frans Verdoorn

No. 31

NOMENCLATURE OF PLANTS

A Text for the Application by the
Case Method
of the International Code of
Botanical Nomenclature

HAROLD ST. JOHN

G. P. WILDER PROFESSOR OF BOTANY
UNIVERSITY OF HAWAII, AND
BOTANIST, B. P. BISHOP MUSEUM, HONOLULU

THE RONALD PRESS COMPANY · NEW YORK

Copyright, © , 1958, by

THE RONALD PRESS COMPANY

All Rights Reserved

Library of Congress Catalog Card Number: 58-11743
Printed in the United States of America

PREFACE

In recent times systematic botany has gained increased recognition, and this is reflected by the ever-larger number of schools, colleges, and universities that include it in their formal program of instruction. The taxonomic part is taught at length by lecture, textbook, laboratory work, and on field excursions.

On the other hand, nomenclature is usually covered briefly in a week or two of lectures. These are mostly historical in viewpoint, as opposed to practical. Such lectures are of value and are interesting, but the student does not gain a detailed knowledge of the content of the laws or the nomenclatural procedure under them as codified in the International Code of Botanical Nomenclature. He does not learn the basic principles of nomenclature. Usually his only real contact with it is by a chance overhearing of an argument between two of his instructors as to which is the correct name of a particular plant. Some taxonomists announce to their students that nomenclature is an evil, though they admit its necessity. They argue that a botanist should spend all his time studying the plants themselves, and that time spent on nomenclature is time wasted.

On the contrary, a taxonomic report published with the taxonomy or classification well done, but the nomenclature incomplete or incorrect, is not authoritative and must be done over again by some competent investigator.

After a short, well-directed study, nomenclature becomes first interesting, then fascinating. Its study reveals much of the development of botany, and it gives a familiarity with the beginnings of the science, the pioneer workers on, and the great books of, our science.

For more than a decade the writer has taught a course on botanical nomenclature at the University of Hawaii. The response by the students has been such as to cause him to expand the material and to present it in book form so that it may be used by other teachers of systematic botany.

The subject is the application of the laws of botanical nomenclature. As in teaching civil law, the best method of instruction is by the case method. Each student who is assigned a case investigates it, finds and evaluates each publication cited, searches for other pertinent facts, for other names, such as homonyms, nomina conservanda, etc., then, when ready, he reports on the case. The student gives his interpretations before the class, the members of which serve as the jury. Queries and arguments bring out the features of the case. The instructor, serving as judge, guides the discussion, confirms the opinion of the jury, or, if necessary, gives his own judgment. This method of presentation has proved stimulating to the individual students.

The cases here given are grouped in chapters. Those in Chapter 2 illustrate all of the articles and recommendations of the last International Code of Botanical Nomenclature. Chapter 3 contains mostly cases on the Cryptogams. Chapter 4 and the succeeding chapters contain additional cases, useful for large classes, or as alternative cases, or for advanced study. No one library contains all the botanical books. The large and active botanical centers all have extensive libraries that are adequate. Young or small institutions have much smaller book collections, but each is building a working library. In selecting cases, especially in Chapter 2, an effort has been made to stress those depending on books that are common and widely available either as originals or as reprints. If the student finds only three of the four cited books, he will still profit by investigating and reporting on this evidence as it pertains to the case. Also, interlibrary loans are generally available, and in lack of these, the reference from almost any book can be had in microfilm at low cost.

At each successive International Botanical Congress, amendments to the Code are adopted. At the recent ones these changes in the laws have been minor, due to the precise and well-framed nature of the laws of the Code and to its world-wide acceptance. Even though amendments adopted at future Congresses may alter the present solution of a few of these problems, the cases will nevertheless continue to be useful for the illustration of the application of the laws of nomenclature. The writer has applied the current botanical laws to the 896 cases here presented. A solution of each case, with the numbers of the articles and recommendations applicable, could have been included. However, it was felt that this would reduce the value of the book as a textbook for instruction in nomenclature. Hence, the decision as to the correct solution of each case is left freely open to each class, with the professor and students acting as judge and jury.

In completing this text the author has benefited by the kind assistance of many people: directors, curators, librarians, and other staff officers of herbaria in America and Europe. Their assistance is gratefully acknowledged. Outstanding was the bibliographic and nomenclatural aid from former colleagues or students, particularly Dr. D. P. Rogers of the University of Illinois, Dr. R. S. Cowan of the Smithsonian Institution, and Dr. G. L. Webster of the Harvard University Herbarium. Major assistance was also received in the privilege kindly granted of verifying bibliographic references by allowing the author full access to the rich libraries of the Gray Herbarium of Harvard University, the New York Botanical Garden, the Royal Botanic Gardens at Kew, and the Conservatoire et Jardin Botanique in Geneva.

Harold St. John

Honolulu, Hawaii
  July, 1958

CONTENTS

NOMENCLATURE OF PLANTS

CHAPTER 1

INTRODUCTION

Nomenclature is an inseparable and necessary part of the science and art of systematic botany. On a factual basis, such as the distinctive morphology, samples of a plant population are classified as a distinct unit, now called a taxon. On evaluation of its resemblances to, and differences from, other taxa, the botanist decides upon its taxonomy, that is, the placement of the taxon into the general system of classification. When this placement is determined, then the correct scientific name, according to plant nomenclature, must be found. The existing names must be judged as to whether or not they are effectively published, validly published, and with priority. If no available name exists, a new one must be formed. These two steps in the establishment of a taxon are, respectively, taxonomic and nomenclatural. Systematic work is correctly and fully done only when both of these steps are properly carried out.

Though they have had various and even identical definitions in botanical texts and dictionaries, the following botanical terms are used in this text as here defined:

Systematic botany or *systematics* embraces the whole field of systematic work, including the placing of an individual plant into a category of classification or taxon, the assignment of the taxon into the system of orderly arrangement or phylogeny, and the selection of a scientific name. This is divisible into the two following parts:

Taxonomy deals with the placement of a plant into its smallest taxon, and that taxon into the hierarchy of larger ones in the system. All such modern systems are phylogenetic in character.

Nomenclature deals with the selection of the correct scientific name for a plant when placed in a particular taxon, in conformity with the legal requirements, that is, with the articles and rec-

ommendations of the last International Code of Botanical Nomenclature.

The new terms *neosystematics* and *biosystematy* are not used
here, as they seem based on an overemphasis of the fact that in
recent times genetics and ecology have provided some new evidence to be included with the morphologic in reaching taxonomic
judgements.

A very effective way of training botanical students in nomenclature is by having them take part in the doing of it. This is
easily arranged and supervised by assigning the students jointly
or singly to solve a series of nomenclatural cases. Each student
who is assigned a case investigates it, finds and evaluates each
publication cited, searches for other pertinent facts, for other
names, such as homonyms, nomina conservanda, etc., then, when
ready, reports on the case. The student gives his interpretations
before the class, the members of which serve as the jury. Queries and arguments bring out the features of the case. The instructor, serving as judge, guides the discussion, confirms the
opinion of the jury, or, if necessary, gives his own judgement.
This method of presentation has proved stimulating to the individual students.

There is given below, as an example, the case of *Cydonia
Cydonia*, and the process, step by step, of its investigation and
solution. The others can be digested and solved in a similar
way, and the study of a series of these cases will aid in giving
students a sounder training in botany.

Solution of a Sample Nomenclatural Case

Cydonia Cydonia (L.) Pers., Syn. Pl. 2: 40, 1807.
Pyrus Cydonia L., Sp. Pl. 480, 1753.
Cydonia Oblonga Mill., Gard. Dict., ed. 8, Cydonia No. 1, 1768.
C. vulgaris Pers., Syn. Pl. 2: Corrigenda for p. 40, 1807.

The earliest of these names is *Pyrus Cydonia*, which is found
in Linnaeus' *Species Plantarum*, 1753. There on page 480
Linnaeus published this name for the quince tree, found on the
rocky banks of the Danube. This name appeared in his printed
book, which was offered for sale in 1753, hence, it was effectively published, under Art. 29 (1956), which states, ''Publica-

tion is effected, under this Code, only by distribution of printed matter (through sale, exchange, or gift) to the general public or at least to botanical institutions with libraries accessible to botanists generally." The name was validly published, under Art. 13, which provides, "Valid publication . . . is treated as beginning, . . . a. Spermatophyta and Pteridophyta, 1 May 1753 (Linnaeus, *Species Plantarum*, ed. 1)."

It is published with references to earlier printed descriptions in two of his own books, one book by Royen, and one by Bauhin. This satisfies Art. 32(2), which requires that, "In order to be validly published, a name of a taxon of recent plants must be both (1) effectively published . . . and (2) accompanied by a description of the taxon or by a reference (direct or indirect) to a previously and effectively published description of it."

It is validly published with the new specific epithet to be associated as a binomial with the generic name, under Art. 32, fourth paragraph, which reads, "A combination is not validly published unless the author definitely indicates that the epithet or epithets concerned are to be used in that particular combination. . . . Examples, In Linnaeus' *Species Plantarum* the placing of the epithet in the margin opposite the name of the genus clearly indicates the combination intended."

Cydonia Oblonga Miller, published in his great *Gardeners Dictionary*, ed. 8, 1768, was effectively published. It contained a description and the common name, Quince-tree. It also gave a reference to the earlier *Cydonia fructu oblongo laeviori* of Tournefort's *Institutiones Rei Herbarii*, 632, a book published in 1700. There the genus was described and illustrated, and the name quoted above given for the quince. This was published before the starting date of botanical nomenclature, 1753 (Art. 13), and the species was given not a binomial but a polynomial, which is now illegitimate under Art. 23, which states: "The name of a species is a binary combination consisting of the name of the genus followed by a single specific epithet." Consequently, the name published by Tournefort is illegitimate, but the description and figure given by him can be cited as the basis of a binomial that was published in or after 1753. Miller's *Gardeners Dictionary* was without numbered pages, instead it was organized like an encyclopaedia, with the entries in alphabetical order. Under *Cydonia*, with three species, it said, "The species are, 1. Cydonia (*Oblonga*) foliis oblongo-ovatis subtus tomentosis, pomis oblongis basi productis. Quince-tree with oblong oval leaves, woolly on their under side, and an oblong fruit lengthened at the base." Miller discussed the grouping by Linnaeus of the apple, pear, and quince in the same genus, *Pyrus*. He opined that the quince and the pear were nearly allied botanically, but the apple not so. Then, in the section on propagation, he continued, "As the Pear will take upon the Quince by grafting or budding, and so vice versa, we may conclude there is a near alliance between them; but as neither of these will take upon the Apple, nor that upon either of these, so we should separate them under different genera, as will be further mentioned under the article Malus." Under the generic heading *Cydonia*, Miller gave references to *Cydonia* Tourn., and *Pyrus* of Linnaeus in his *Genera Plantarum*, 1754. Consequently *Pyrus Cydonia* L. and *Cydonia Oblonga* Mill. are synonymous in that they are based in part upon the same Tournefort reference. The other references also are accepted as applying to this same species.

The issue as to whether the quince, the pear, and the apple are to be left in a single genus is a taxonomic one. As to the apple and pear, the question is still moot, but there is a consensus of interpretation that the quince forms a separate genus, as can be seen in the manuals, encyclopaedias, and systems of botany. As a genus separated from *Pyrus*, the first validly published name is *Cydonia* [Tourn.] Mill. The *Index Kewensis* gives Miller's *Gardeners Dictionary*, ed. 6, as the place of origin of this generic name. However, this edition appeared in 1752, a pre-Linnaean date, hence the name is illegitimate, under Art. 13, which, as quoted above, establishes 1 May 1753 as the starting point for scientific botanical nomenclature. The reference given in this case, Miller's ed. 8, of 1768, is the first valid publication of a generic name for this group as a genus.

Miller's name *Cydonia* (*Oblonga*) *foliis oblongo-ovatis*, etc., might be considered a polynomial, but examination will show that the latter phrases were the description and the word (*Oblonga*) was the epithet for the species. It was a better and more economical arrangement with the epithet in parentheses following the generic name, than was Linnaeus' method of placing the epithet singly in the margin. That Miller's method was an acceptable indication of a binomial is stated in Art. 32, Examples, "The same result is attained in Miller's *Gardeners Dictionary*, ed. 8, by the inclusion of the epithet in parentheses immediately after the name of the genus, . . ." The epithet *Oblonga*, not being the name of a person, or a vernacular name, or a former generic name, should now be written with small letters, under Rec. 73F, which states, "All specific and infraspecific epithets should be written with a small initial letter, . . ."

Cydonia Cydonia (L.) Pers. was a combination, made by Persoon in 1807, of the oldest specific epithet (1753) under the valid generic name *Cydonia* (1768). When Persoon did this, the practice was legal. Now, all the recent codes of nomenclature have legislated against this kind of action. The most recent code, that of 1954 (published in 1956) asserts, Art. 70, "epithet is illegitimate . . . (4) When it exactly repeats the generic name, . . ." These tautonyms are now invalid, so, though the epithet *Cydonia* of Linnaeus was the first valid name, it cannot be used, as it is illegitimate if combined under the genus *Cydonia* as *Cydonia Cydonia*.

The *Index Kewensis* gives *Cydonia vulgaris* Pers. as having been published by Persoon on page 40 of his *Synopsis*. That is incorrect. But C. K. Schneider's *Illustriertes Handbuch der Laubholzkunde* 1: 654, 1906, gives the reference as the Errata in Persoon's *Synopsis*. That is correct, and there Persoon says, "ob infer. loco *Cydonia* leg. vulgaris," so Persoon's corrected name for the quince was *Cydonia vulgaris* (1807). Under the species he gives a description, and a reference to *Pyrus* L., which ties his new name back to the original *Pyrus Cydonia* L. By our present rules Persoon was correct in avoiding a tautonym, but he should have adopted the earliest specific epithet, in this case, *oblonga* of Miller (1768). The two epithets are certainly synonyms, both being traceable back to Linnaeus and to Tournefort. Art. 11 provides, "Each order or taxon of lower rank with a particular circumscription, position, and rank can bear only one correct name, . . . For any taxon below the rank of genus inclusive, the correct name is the earliest legitimate one validly published with the same rank, except in cases of limitation of priority by conservation . . ." Hence, *vulgaris* of Persoon is illegitimate, *oblonga* of Miller being earlier and available.

The correct scientific name of the quince, when classified as a separate genus, is *Cydonia oblonga* Mill. (1768).

The solution of this nomenclatural case brings the student in contact with several of the fundamental and great botanical books. The correct interpretation of this case rests upon an ability to read scientific books in several languages, an understanding of the principles of priority, synonymy, and the regulations governing the binomial system and tautonyms. Other principles, laws, and recommendations are illustrated by the other cases. Often a case will involve many of the articles and recommendations of the International Code of Botanical Nomenclature.

Useful Publications

The publications useful to a student of nomenclature are many, too many to be listed here. However, a selection of the most serviceable ones is classified and listed below.

Indexes

Andrews, H. N., Jr. Index of Generic Names of Fossil Plants, 1820-1950. U. S. Geol. Surv., Bul. 1,013. 1955.

Gray Herbarium card index of new genera, species and varieties of American plants, 1885- .

Merrill, E. D. Index Rafinesquianus. 1949.

PHANEROGAMS

Index Kewensis 1-4. Supplements 1-11- . 1895- .

FILICINAE

Christensen, C. Index Filicum, and Supplements. 1906, 1913, 1917, 1934.

MARSILEACEAE AND SALVINIACEAE

Reed, C. F., Index Marsileata et Salviniata. Sociedade Broteriana, Bol. II, 28: 5-61. 1954.

LYCOPODIUM

Herter, W. (or Guilemus). Index Lycopodiorum. 1949.

Herter, W. Systema Lycopodiorum. 1949-50.

ISOËTALES
Reed, C. F. Index Isoëtales. Sociedade Broteriana, Bol. II, 27: 1-72. 1953.

OTHER FERN ALLIES
None.

LICHENS
Zahlbruckner, A. Catalogus Lichenum Universalis, 10 vol. 1921-1940.

FUNGI
Saccardo, P. A. Sylloge Fungorum. 18 vol. 1882-1906.

ALGAE
de Toni, G. B. Sylloge Algarum. 6 vol. 1889-1924.

DESMIDIACEAE
Norstedt, C. F. O. Index desmidiacearum citiationibus locuple-tissimus atque bibliographia, and supplementum. 1896, 1908.

BACTERIA
None, but see Bergey, D. H. Manual of Descriptive Bacteriol-ogy. 1949.

Systems

Bentham, G., and Hooker, J. D. Genera Plantarum. 3 vol. 1862-1883.

De Candolle, A. P., and A. Prodromus systematis naturalis regni vegetabilis. 17 vol., 4 vol. index. 1824-1873.

Engler, A., and Prantl, K. Die Natürliche Pflanzenfamilien. Ed. 1, 23 vol., 1887-1915. Ed. 2, 1924- .

Engler, A. Das Pflanzenreich. 1900- .

Hutchinson, J. The Families of Flowering Plants. 2 vol. 1926, 1934.

Johnson, A. M. Taxonomy of Flowering Plants. 1931.

Rendle, A. B. The Classification of Flowering Plants. 2 vols. 1904, 1925.

Warming, E. A Handbook of Systematic Botany. Ed. by M. C. Potter, 1904.

Wettstein, R. Handbuch der Systematischen Botanik. Ed. 4, 2 vols. 1933, 1935.

Nomenclature Catalogues

Pfeiffer, L.   Nomenclator botanicus.   3 vol. in 4.   1873–1874.
Up to the end of 1858 this alphabets all names from those of
classes down to those of sections.

Steudel, E.   Nomenclator Botanicus.   Ed. 1, 1824.   Ed. 2, 2
vols., 1840–41.

Dictionaries

Willis, J. C.   A Dictionary of the Flowering Plants and Ferns.
6th ed.   1948.

Nomenclature Code

International Code of Botanical Nomenclature adopted by the
Eighth International Botanical Congress.   Paris, July, 1954.
Edited by J. Lanjouw *et al.*, Regnum Vegetabile 8: 1–338,
1956.   Utrecht, I. A. P. T.

International Code of Nomenclature for Cultivated Plants, Regnum
Vegetabile 10: 1–28, 1958.

Bibliographies

Biological Abstracts.   1926–.

Botanical Abstracts.   1918–1926.

Botanisches Centralblatt.   1880–.

British Museum of Natural History, Catalogue of Library.   8 vol.,
including 3 Supplements.   1903–1940.

International Catalogue of Scientific Literature, Botany.   Covering 1900–1913.

Jackson, B. D.   Guide to Literature of Botany.   1881.

Just's Botanischer Jahresbericht.   1873–.

Kew.   Catalogue of the Library of the Royal Botanic Gardens.
Kew Bul. Misc. Inf., Add. Ser. 3.   1899.   Suppl.   1919.

Merrill, E. D., and Walker, E. H.   Botanical Bibliography of the
Pacific.   U. S. Natl. Herb., Contr. 30(1).   1947.

Pritzel, G. A.   Thesaurus Literaturae Botanicae.   Ed. 2.   1871.

Rehder, A.   Bradley Bibliography of Woody Plants.   5 vols.   1911–
1918.

Rehder, A.   Bibliography of Cultivated Trees and Shrubs.   1949.

Royal Society Catalogue of Scientific Literature. 19 vols. Covering 1800–1900.

Guide to Floras

Blake, S. F., and Atwood, A. C. Geographical Guide to Floras of the World. Pt. 1, U. S. Dept. Agric., Misc. Publ. 401. 1942.

Cultivated Plants

Bailey, L. H. Manual of Cultivated Plants. Rev. ed. 1949.

Bailey, L. H. Standard Cyclopedia of Horticulture. 3 vols. 1928, and later reprintings.

Rehder, A. Manual of Cultivated Trees and Shrubs hardy in North America. Ed. 2. 1940.

CHAPTER 2

CASE
1. *Sida Holtzii* F. Muell. (in herb.) ex E. G. Baker, Jour. Bot.
   Brit. For. 30: 325, 1892.*

2. *Pleiogynium Solandri* (Benth.) Engler in DC., Monogr. Phan.
   4: 255, pl. 7, fig. 1-10, 1883.
   Spondias Solandri Benth., Fl. Austral. 1: 492, 1863.
   S. acida Soland. ex Benth., Fl. Austral. 1: 492, 1863.
   Owenia cerasifera F. Muell., Hooker's Jour. Bot. & Kew
   Miscel. 9: 305, 1857.
   S. pleiogyna F. Muell., Fragm. Phytogr. Austral. 4: 78, 1863-
   1864.
   Icica ? Timoriensis DC., Prodr. 2: 78, 1825.
   P. timoriense (DC.) Leenhouts, Blumea 7: 159, 1952.

3. *Phleum pratense* L. Race II—*P. nodosum* L. (Pro specie),
   β *intermedium* Nob., Rouy, Fl. de France 14: 49-50,
   1913.
   P. pratense L., Sp. Pl. 59, 1753.
   P. nodosum L., Syst. Veg., ed. 10, 871, 1759.
   P. intermedium Jordan ex F. W. Schultz, Fl. France et
   Allemagne, Archives 1: 325, (1842-1848) = [1854].

4. *Phyllamphora mirabilis* Lour., Fl. Cochinch. 606, 1790.
   Nepenthes Phyllamphora Willd., Sp. Pl. of L., ed. 4 by Willd.,
   4: 874, 1805.
   N. mirabilis (Lour.) Druce, Bot. Exch. Club Brit., Rept.
   1916: 637, 1917.

*Customary abbreviations of the authors' names are used in the bibliographic
citations. For books the key words of the titles are used in full or in abbre-
viation. Magazine titles are also abbreviated, except where it is necessary
to cite them more fully. The words "plate," "plates," "tables," "tafeln,"
etc., are shortened to pl.; figures are shortened to fig. Roman numbers of
volumes or plates are changed to Arabic numbers, except where confusion
might result, but they are retained for a magazine series number and for the
pages of an introduction so numbered.

N. mirabilis (Lour.) Merr., Interpr. Rumph. Herb. Amboinense
242, 1917.

5. *Convolvulus sepium* L. β *Americanus* Sims, Curtis's Bot.
Mag. 19: pl. 732, 1804.
Calystegia sepium (L.) R. Br. β *rosea* Choisy in DC., Prodr.
9: 433, 1845.

6. *Collinsia* J. Agardh, Analecta Algol. cent. 5: 77-79, 1899.
Collinsia Nutt., Acad. Nat. Sci. Phila., Jour. 1: 190, pl. 9,
1817.
Collinsiae Mack. in Britton & Brown, Ill. Fl. N. U. S. Can.,
ed. 2, 1: 353, 1913.
Carex Collinsii Nutt., Gen. N. Am. Pl. 2: 205, 1818.
Collinsonia L., Gen. Pl., ed. 5, 16, 1754.
See Silva, Univ. Calif., Publ. Bot. 25: 284, 1952.

7. *Cicuta maculata* L., Sp. Pl. 256, 1753.
See Coulter & Rose, U. S. Natl. Herb., Contr. 7: 97-98,
1900;
Fernald, Rhodora 41: 439-440, 1939.

8. *Thelpyteris* Schmidel, Icon. Pl., ed. 2, 45, pl. 11, 13, 1762.
Dryopteris Adans., Fam. Pl. 2: 21, 1763.
Nephrodium Rich., Cat. Jard. Med. Paris, 1801.
See Nakai, Bot. Mag. Tokyo 40: 61, 1926;
Mackenzie, Am. Fern. Jour. 17: 117, 1927;
Fernald & Weatherby, Rhodora 31: 21-36, pl. 179-180,
1929; also as Gray Herb., Contr. n.s. 83: 21-36, pl.
179-180, 1929.

9. *Blechnum orientale* L., Sp. Pl. 1,077, 1753.
B. occidentale L., Sp. Pl. 1,077, 1753.

10. *Englemannia* Gray ex Nutt., Am. Phil. Soc., Trans. II, 7:
343-344, 1841.
Engelmannia T. & G., Fl. N. Am. 2: 283, 1841.
Angelandra Endl., Gen. Pl. Suppl. (Mantissa Bot. Alt.) 3:
69, 1843.
Engelmannia Klotzsch, in Wiegmann's Archiv für Naturgesch.
7: 253, 1841.
Engelmannia Pfeiff., Bot. Zeit. 3: 673, 1845.

11. *Ceodes Umbellifera* J. R. & G. Forst., Char. Gen. Pl. Mar.
Austral. 142, pl. 71, 1776.

C. umbellata J. R. & G. Forst. emend. G. Forst., Fl. Ins.
Austral. Prodr. 93, 1786.

Pisonia umbellata (J. R. & G. Forst.) Seem., Bonplandia 10:
154, 1862.

12. *Houstonia patens* Ell. var. *pusilla* Gray, Syn. Fl. N. Am.
1(2): 25, 1884.

H. pusilla Schoepf, Reise 2: 306, 1788.

H. pusilla J. F. Gmel., Syst. Nat. of L., ed. 13 by J. F.
Gmel., 2: 236, (1788) = [1791].

H. pusilla Schoepf forma *rosea* Steyerm., Rhodora 41: 585,
1939.

H. pygmaea C. H. & M. T. Mueller, Torrey Bot. Club, Bul.
63: 33–34, 1936.

H. Taylorae Fosberg, Field & Lab. 17: 169, 1949.

Hedyotis ? rosea Raf., Fl. Ludovic. 77, 1817.

13. *Brodiaea Orcuttii* (Greene) Baker, Gard. Chron. III, 20: 214,
1896.

Hookera Orcuttii Greene, Calif. Acad. Sci., Bul. 2: 138, 1886.

H. multipedunculata Abrams, Torrey Bot. Club, Bul. 32: 537,
1905.

14. *Wyethia amplexicaulis* Nutt., Am. Phil. Soc., Trans. II, 7:
352–353, 1840.

Espeletia amplexicaulis Nutt., Acad. Nat. Sci. Phila., Jour.
7: 38, 1834.

See Weber, Am. Midl. Nat. 35: 441, 1946.

15. *Puccinia-Convolvuli* (Pers.) Cast., Obs. Pl. Acot. Urédinées
1: 16, 1842.

Vredo betae β Vredo Conuoluuli Pers., Syn. Fung. 221, 1801.

See Jackson, Mycologia 23: 495, 1931;
Rickett, Taxon 4: 185–188, 1955.

16. *Cracca* L., Gen. Pl., ed. 5, 333, 1754; Sp. Pl. 752, 1753.

Cracca Benth. in Benth. & Oersted, Kjoeb. Vidensk., Meddel.
1853: 8, 1854.

Cracca L. sensu Ktze., Rev. Gen. 1: 173–176, 1891.

Galega L., Syst. Nat., ed. 10, 2: 1,172, 1759; Gen. Pl., ed.
5, 320, 1754; ed. 6, 384, 1764; Syst. Nat., ed. 13, 2:
496–497, 1770.

Tephrosia Fers., Syn. Pl. 2: 328, 1807.

Benthamantha Alefeld, Bonplandia 10: 264, 1862.
Brittonamra Ktze., Rev. Gen. 164, 1891.
See Wood, Rhodora 51: 197–199, 1949.

17. *Geitonoplesium cymosum* (R. Br.) A. Cunn. var. *timorense*
(Ridley) Schlittler, Bot. Mus. Univ. Zürich, Mitt. 189:
228, 238, 1951.
Luzuriaga cymosa R. Br., Prodr. Fl. Nov. Holl. 282,
1810.
Eustrephus timorensis Ridley in H. O. Forbes, Nat. Wand.
East. Archip. 520, 1885.

18. *Convolvulus tiliaefolius* Desr. in Lam., Encyc. Méth. Bot. 3:
544, 1789.
Ipomoea grandiflora Lam., Tabl. Encyc. 1: 467, 1791.
Stictocardia tiliaefolia (Choisy) Hallier f., Engl. Bot. Jahrb.
18: 159, 1894.
Convolvulus grandiflorus L. f., Suppl. 136, 1781.
Stictocardia tiliifolia (Desr.) Hallier f. emend. Oostr. &
Hoogl., Fl. Males. 4: 491, 1953.
See van Ooststroom, Blumea 3: 577, 1940.

19. *Elsholtzia* Willd. in Roem. & Usteri, Mag. 4(11): 3, 1790.
Elsbolzia Reichb., Consp. 116, (1828) = [1829].
Elsholtia Koch, Syn. Fl. Germ., ed. 2, 631, 1844.
Elschotzia Brongn., Enum. Gen. Pl. 68, 1843.
Elsholzia Moench, Meth. Pl. Hort. Bot. Marburg, 389, 1794.
Elshotzia Roxb., Fl. Ind., ed. Carey, 3: 4, 1832.
Elssholzia Garcke, Fl. Deutschl., ed. 6, 307, 1863; ed. 19,
479, 1903.
Eschscholzia Cham. in Nees, Hor. Phys. Berol. 73, index,
1820.
Eschholzia Cham. in Nees, Hor. Phys. Berol., pl. 15, 1820.
Eschholtzia Reichb., Consp. 187, 1828.
Escholtzia Dum., Anal. Fam. Pl. 52, 1829.
Eschscholtzia Cham., Linnaea 8: 464, 1833.
Eschsholzia DC., Prodr. 3: 344, 1828.

20. *Delisea* Lamx., Dict. Sci. Nat. 13: 41–42, 1819.
Delissea Gaud., Bot. Voy. Freyc. Uranie 457, pl. 6, 78,
(1826) = [1829].
Delisea Fée, Essai Cryptog. Écorces, pp. LXIV–LXV, 151,
1824.

Delitschia Auerswald, Hedwigia 5: 49, 1866.
    See Silva, Taxon 6: 143, 1957.
21. *Viola Chamissoniana* Ging. var. *beta* Hbd. ex MacCaughey,
    Torreya 18: 5, 1918.
    V. Chamissoniana Ging. β var. Hbd., Fl. Hawaiian Is. 17,
    1888.
22. *Scaevola Chamissoniana* Gaud. var. *typica* Hochr., Candollea
    5: 295, 1934.
23. *Absinthium* Tourn., Inst. Rei Herb. 1: 457–459, pl. 260,
    1700.
    Absinthium [Tourn.] ex L., Syst. Nat., ed. 1: 1735; Gen. Pl.,
        ed. 5, 367, 1754.
    Absynthium Gaertn., Meyer & Scherb., Fl. Wetterau 3: 196,
        1801'
    Absinthium Gaertn., Fruct. 2: 393, pl. 164, 1791.
    Absinthium Adans., Fam. Pl. 2: 120, 1763.
    Artemisia L. sect. *Absinthium* Besser ex DC., Fl. France 4:
        189, 1805; DC., Prodr. 6: 120, 1837.
      See Gray, Syn. Fl. N. Am. 1(2): 369, 1884;
          Hall & Clements, Carnegie Inst. Wash., Publ. 326:
              46, 106, 1923.
24. *Apium Petroselinum* L., Sp. Pl. 264, 1753.
    A. latifolium Mill., Gard. Dict., ed. 8, Apium No. 3, 1768.
    A. crispum Mill., Gard. Dict., ed. 8, Apium No. 2, 1768.
    A. hortense, seu Petroselinum vulgo Bauhin, Pinax 153,
        1671.
    A. vel Petroselinum crispum Bauhin, Pinax 153, 1671.
    A. hortense latifolium Bauhin, Pinax 153, 1671.
    Petroselinum hortense Hoffm., Gen. Pl. Umbellif. 163, 166,
        XXV, pl. 1A, fig. 7, pl. 1B, fig. 4, 1814.
    P. sativum Hoffm., Gen. Pl. Umbellif. 177 (in indice), 78,
        1814.
    P. Petroselinum (L.) Karst., Deutschl. Fl., ed. 2, 2: 394,
        1895.
    P. crispum (Mill.) A. W. Hill, Kew Hand-List Herb. Pl., ed.
        3, 122, 1925.
    Apium sativum Hoffm. var. *Petroselinum crispum* Nym.,
        Conspec. Fl. Eur. 2: 309, 1879.

See Airy-Shaw, Kew Bul. 257, 1938; 168, 1939;
   Mansfeld, Fedde Repert. Sp. Nov. 46: 307, 1939;
   Hill, Harvard Bot. Mus. Leafl. 10: 163, 1942;
   Hara, Bot. Mag. Tokyo 61: 716, 1948;
   Furtado, Gardens' Bul. 12: 345, 1949.

25. *Euonymus* [Tourn.] L., Gen. Pl., ed. 5, 91, 1754.
   Evonymus L., Sp. Pl. 197, 1753.
   See Rickett, Taxon 4: 185–188, 1955;
   Lawrence, Baileya 3: 113, 1955.

26. *Jungermannia frondibus supra bipinnatis apice floriferis,
   foliolis ciliatis* L., Sp. Pl. 1,132, 1753.

27. *Leuchorchis straminea* (Fern.) Löve, Bot. Notis. 1950(1): 36,
   1950.
   L. albida (L.) E. Mey. ssp. *straminea* (Fern.) Löve, Bot.
   Notis. 1950(1): 36, 1950.
   Habenaria straminea Fern., Rhodora 28: 174, 1926.

28. *Pelea brownii* F. Br., Bishop Mus., Bul. 84: 6, 1931.

29. *Acosta* Ruiz & Pavon, Fl. Peruv. Chil., Prodr. 1, pl. 1, 1794.
   Moutabea Aubl., Hist. Pl. Guian. 2: 679, pl. 274, 1775.

30. *Kingdon-Wardia* Marquand, Linn. Soc. Lond. Bot., Jour. 48:
   207, 1929.

31. *Lepturus reptans* Guillaumin, Fl. Nouv.-Calédonie 32, 1948.

32. *Uvularia pudica* (Walt.) Fern., Rhodora 41: 536, 1939.
   Anonymos pudic. Walt., Fl. Carol. 123, 1788.
   Uvularia puberula Michx., Fl. Bor.-Am. 1: 199, 1803.

33. *Circaea lutetiana* L. β *canadensis* L., Sp. Pl. 9, 1753.
   C. lutetiana canadensis L. ex Michx., Fl. Bor.-Am. 1: 17,
   1803.
   C. intermedia Ehrh., Beitr. Naturk. 4: 42, 1789.
   C. quadrisulcata (Maxim.) Franch. & Sav. var. *canadensis*
   (L.) Hara, Rhodora 41: 387, 1939.
   C. lutetiana L. var. *quadrisulcata* (Maxim.) Maxim. ex
   Aschers. & Magnus, Bot. Zeit. 28: 783, 1870.
   C. latifolia Hill, Brit. Herb. 138, 1756.
   C. lutetiana L. forma *quadrisulcata* Maxim., Prim. Fl. Amur.
   106, 1859.

C. lutetiana L. ssp. *quadrisulcata* Maxim. ex Aschers. &
        Magnus, Bot. Zeit. 28: 787, 1870.
C. mollis Sieb. & Zucc. var. *Maximowiczii* Lévl., Bul. Geog⁻.
        Bot. (21:) = [22:] 223, 1912.
C. Maximowiczii (Lévl.) Hara, Jour. Jap. Bot. 10: 598, fig.
        13, 1934.

34. *Platyspermum* Hoffm., Gen. Pl. Umbellif. 64, 1814.
        Platyspermum Hook., Fl. Bor.-Am. 1: 68, pl. 18, fig. B, 1829.
        Idahoa scapigera (Hook.) Nels. & Macbr., Bot. Gaz. 56: 474,
        1913.
        Carex Idahoa L. H. Bailey, Bot. Gaz. 21: 5, 1896.

35. *Cotyledon* Tourn. ex L., Gen. Pl., ed. 5, 196, 1754; Sp. Pl.
        429–430, 1753.

36. *Quercus marilandica* Muenchh., Hausv. 5: 253, 1770.
        Q. Marylandica Muenchh. emend. Britton & Brown, Ill. Fl.
        N. U. S. & Can. 1: 518, fig. 1,235, 1896.

37. *Hypochoeris* L., Gen. Pl., ed. 5, 352, 1754.
        Hypochaeris L., Sp. Pl. 810–811, 1753.

38. *Potamogeton* [Tourn.] ex L., Gen. Pl., ed. 5, 61, 1754.
        Hydrogeton Lour., Fl. Cochinch. 244, 1790.
        Patamogeton Honck., Synops. Pl. Germ. 2: 110, 1793.
        Potamogiton Raf., Med. Repos. New York 5: 354, 1808.
        Potamogetum Clairv., Man. d'herb. Suisse 34, 44, 1811.

39. *Nelumbo lutea* (Willd.) Pers., Syn. Pl. 2: 92, 1807.
        Nelumbium luteum Willd., Sp. Pl. of L., ed. 4 by Willd., 2:
        1,259, 1799.
        Nymphaea pentapetala Walt., Fl. Carol. 155, 1788.
        Nymphaea Nelumbo L. β L., Sp. Pl. 730, 1753.
        Nelumbo pentapetala (Walt.) Fern., Rhodora 36: 23–24, 1934.
        Nelumbo [Tourn.] Adans., Fam. Pl. 2: 73, 76, 1763.
        Nelumbium Juss., Gen. 68, 1789; ed. 2, 76, 1791.
        See Gleason, Phytologia 2: 205–206, 1947.

40. *Eustrephus latifolius* R. Br. ssp. *angustifolius* (R. Br.)
        Schlittler, Bot. Mus. Univ. Zürich, Mitt. 189: 213, 1951.
        E. angustifolius R. Br., Prodr. Fl. Nov. Holl. 281, 1810.

41. *Spongia oculata* L., Sp. Pl. 1,170, 1753.
        Spongia oculata L., Syst. Nat., ed. 10, 2: 1,348, 1759.

Haliclona oculata (Linnaeus). See de Laubenfels, Harvard
Mus. Comp. Zool., Bul. 103(1): 9, 1949.

42. *Clavaria* [Vaill.] ex L., Gen. Pl., ed. 5, 493, 1754.
Clavaria Stackh., Nereis Brit., ed. 2, X, 1816.
Clavaria [Vaill.] ex Fr., Syst. Mycol. 1: 465, 1821.
Gelidium Lamx., Essai Thalass., in Paris Mus. Nat. Hist.,
Ann. 20: 128–129, 1813.
See Doty, Lloydia 2: 126–127, 1948.

43. *Dioscorea* affinis *alata* L., ex Christophersen, Bishop Mus.,
Bul. 128: 51–52, fig. 7, 1935.

44. *Balduina* Nutt., Gen. N. Am. Pl. 2: 175, 1818.
Baldwinia Nutt. emend. Gray, Syn. Fl. N. Am. 1(2): 302, 1884.

45. *Zanthoxylum Kauaense* Gray, U. S. Expl. Exped. Bot.
Phanerogamia 15(1): 354, 1854.
Zanthoxylum Kauaiense Gray emend. Hbd., Fl. Haw. Ids. 73,
1888.
Z. Kauaiense Gray emend. Hbd., γ Hbd., Fl. Haw. Ids. 74,
1888.
Fagara kauaiense (Gray) Engler, Natür. Pflanzenfam., ed. 2,
19a: 217, 1931.
F. kauaiense (Gray) Engler var. *kohuana* Skottsb., Göteborg
Bot. Trädg., Medded. 15: 381, 1944; on p. 518 as
kohuaana.

46. *Abies* (*Canadensis*) foliis linearibus obtusiusculis submem-
branaceis. Mill., Gard. Dict., ed. 8, Abies No. 4, 1768.
Pinus glauca Moench, Verzeichn. Baeume Weissenst. 73,
1785.
Picea canadensis (Michx.) Link, Linnaea 15: 524, 1841.
Picea canadensis (Mill.) BSP., Prelim. Cat. Anth. Pterid.
New York 71, 1888.
Picea glauca Beissn., Handb. Conif. 59, 1887.
Picea glauca (Moench) Voss, Deut. Dendrol. Gesell., Mitt.
16: 93, 1907.
See Rehder, Rhodora 17: 59–62, 1915; Arn. Arb., Jour. 1:
57, 1919.

47. Asparagus caule herbaceo erecto, foliis setaceis . . . Mill.,
Gard. Dict., ed. 8, Asparagus No. 1, 1768.

48. *Viola Kauaensis* Gray, U. S. Expl. Exped. Phanerogamia
    15(1): 85, 1854.

   V. Kauensis Gray, Am. Acad. Arts Sci., Proc. 2: 325, 1852.

   V. Kavaiensis Gray ex Mann, Am. Acad. Arts Sci., Proc. 7:
    150, 1867.

   V. Kawaiensis Gray ex Drake, Ill. Fl. Maris Pacif. 108,
    1890.

   V. kauaiensis Gray emend. Skottsb., Göteberg Bot. Trädg.,
    Meddel. 13: 513, 1940

49. *Fimbristylis marquesana* Steud., Syn. Pl. Glum., ed. 2, 2:
    107, 1855.

   F. marquesana Steud. emend. B. D. Jackson, Ind. Kew. 4:
    1,284, 1895; F. Brown, Bishop Mus., Bul. 84: 104, 1931;
    Drake, Fl. Polyn. Fr. 242, 1893.

50. *Sidalcea* Gray, Am. Acad. Arts Sci., Mem. n.s. 4: 18, 1849
    (Pl. Fendler.).

   S. secundiflora Greene, Fl. Francisc. 103, 1891; Man. Bot.
    San Francisc. 65, 1894.

   See Rousch, Mo. Bot. Gard., Ann. 18: 118, 138, 1931.

51. *Cassia hebecarpa* Fern., Rhodora 39: 413, 1937.

   C. nictitans L. var. *hebecarpa* Fern., Rhodora 38: 423, 1936.

52. *Juncus fucensis* St. John, State Coll. Washington, Bot. Dept.,
    Contr. 10: first page, 1928, March 31; British Columbia
    Prov. Mus., Rept. for 1927: E 14, 1928, July.

53. *Rudbeckia columnifera* Nutt., Fraser's Cat. 1813; repr. in
    Pittonia 2: 116–119, 1890. See Nutt., Gen. N. Am. Pl.
    2: 178–179, 1818.

   Rudbeckia columnaris Pursh, Fl. Am. Sept. 575, 1814.

   Ratibida columnifera (Nutt.) Wooton & Standl., U. S. Nat.
    Herb., Contr. 19: 706, 1915.

   Lepachys columnaris (Pursh) T. & G., Fl. N. Am. 2: 313,
    1842.

   Rudbeckia columnaris Sims, Curtis's Bot. Mag. 39: pl. 1,601,
    1813.

   Ratibida columnaris (Sims) D. Don in Sweet, Brit. Fl. Gard.
    7: 361, 1838.

   Ratibida sulcata Raf., Am. Month. Mag. 2: 268, 1818; Jour.
    Phys. 89: 100, 1819.

Obeliscaria columnaris (Pursh) DC., Prodr. 5: 559, 1836.

Obelisteca pinnata (Vent.) Raf., Fl. Ludovic. 73, 1817.

　See Shinners, Rhodora 57: 290–293, 1955;
　　　Graustein, Rhodora 58: 20–22, 1956;
　　　Cronquist *et al.,* Rhodora 58: 23–24, 1956;
　　　Shinners, Rhodora 58: 281–289, 1956;
　　　Cronquist, Rhodora 59: 100, 1957.

54. *Eucanna* Baker, Gard. Chron. 43, 1893; Engler & Prantl, Nat.
　　　Pflanzenfam., ed. 2, 15a: 653, 1930.

　Trialatae Kränzl., Engler's Pflanzenreich IV, fam. 47: 47,
　　　1912.

　Glaucae Kränzl., Engler's Pflanzenreich IV, fam. 47: 47–48,
　　　1912.

55. *Greyiaceae* Hutchins., Fam. Fl. Pl. Dicots. 1: 202, 1926.

　Greyieae Engler & Prantl, Nat. Pflanzenfam. IV, 3(5): 382,
　　　1896.

　Greyia Hook. & Harvey, Dublin Univ. Zool. Bot. Assoc.,
　　　Proc. 1: 137, pl. 13–14, 1858.

　Graya Arn. ex Steud., Nom., ed. 2, 1: 705, 1840.

　Graya Endl., Gen. Suppl. 1: 1,376, [1841].

　Graya Arn. ex Steud., Syn. Pl. Gram. 119, 1855.

　Grayia H. & A., Bot. Beechey Voy. 387, (1832) =[1841].

　Grayia Grove & Brun in A. Schmidt, Atlas der Diatomaceenk.
　　　pl. 172, fig. 11, 1892.

56. *Sesuvium Portulacastrum* L., Syst. Nat., ed. 10, 1,058, 1759;
　　　Sp. Pl., ed. 2, 1: 684, 1762; ed. 3, 1: 684, 1764.

　Portulaca Portulacastrum L., Sp. Pl. 446, 1753.

　Portulacastrum Juss. ex Medic., Phil. Bot. 1: 99, 1789.

57. *Arabis laevigata* (Muhl.) Poir. var. *heterophylla* Farw., Mich.
　　　Acad. Sci., Ann. Rept. 19: 248, 1917.

　A. viridis Harger var. *Deamii* Hopkins, Rhodora 39: 160,
　　　1937.

　A. viridis Harger var. *heterophylla* (Farw.) Farw., Rhodora
　　　41: 80, 1939.

　A. missouriensis Greene var. *Deamii* (Hopkins) Hopkins,
　　　Rhodora 45: 269, 1943.

58. *Rosales* Engler, Natürl. Pflanzenfam., Nachtr. 348, 1897.

59. *Conyzopsis* T. & G., Fl. N. Am. 2: 162, 1841.
   Conyzopsis (T. & G.) Gray, Am. Acad. Arts Sci., Proc. 16:
      99, 1881.

60. *Daboecieae* Cox, Am. Midl. Nat. 39: 238-239, 1948.

61. *Berberis simplex* Newberry, U. S. Natl. Mus., Proc. 5: 514,
      1883.
   Odostemon simplex (Newberry) Cockerell, Am. Mus. Nat.
      Hist., Bul. 24: 91, 1908.
   Mahonia simplex (Newberry) Arnold, Univ. Mich., Mus.
      Paleont., Contr. 5: 58, pl. 1, fig. 1-3, 6-7; pl. 2, fig.
      1-2, 1936.

62. *Yucca glauca* Alliance, J. M. Webber, U. S. Dept. Agric.,
      Monogr. 17: 55, 1953.

63. *Claytonia Washingtoniana* Suksd., Deutsch. Bot. Monatschr.
      16: 220, 1898.
   Montia Washingtoniana Suksd., Deutsch. Bot. Monatschr. 16:
      220, 1898.

64. *Aster nemoralis* Ait., Hort. Kew. 3: 198, 1789.

65. *Bucklandia* Presl, in Sternberg, Versuch Bot. Darstell. Fl.
      Vorwelt xxxiii, 1825 = [1820].
   Bucklandia R. Br., in Wall. Cat. (Num. List Pl. E. Ind.) No.
      7,414, 1832.
   Symingtonia van Steenis, Bot. Néerl., Acta 1: 443-444,
      1952.
      See Taxon 3: 221, 1954.

66. *Liparis Yamadae* Tuyama, Bot. Mag. Tokyo 54: 265, pl. 2n.,
      1940.
   Cestichis Yamadae Tuyama, Bot. Mag. Tokyo 54: 265, pl.
      2n., 1940.

67. *Amarella quinquefida* Gilib., Fl. Lith. Inch. 1: 36, 1781.
   Gentiana Amarella L., Sp. Pl. 230, 1753.

68. *Gentiana Centaurium* L., Sp. Pl. 229, 1753.
   Centaurium minus Garssault, Fig. Pl. Anim. Med. 137, pl.
      206, 1764.
   Erythraea Centaurium (L.) Pers., Syn. Pl. 1: 283, 1805.
   Centauriom Centaurium (L.) W. F. Wight, U. S. Natl. Herb.,
      Contr. 11: 449, 1906.

Centaurium minus Moench, Meth. Pl. Hort. Bot. Marburg 449,
　　1794.

Centaurium umbellatum Gilib., Fl. Lith. 1: 35, 1785.

Centaurium Erythraea Rafn, Danm. og Holst. Fl. 2: 70, 1800.

Chironia Centaurium (L.) F. W. Schmidt, Fl. Boem. 2: 31,
　　1793.

　　See Britten & Rendle, Jour. Bot. Brit. For. 47: 322, 1909;
　　　　Jonker, Nederl. Kruidk., Arch. 57: 184–188, fig. la,
　　　　1950; repr. as Bot. Mus. Herb. Rijksuniv. Utrecht,
　　　　Meded. 99: 184–188, fig. la, 1950;
　　　　A. Robyns, Jard. Bot. État Bruxelles, Bul. 24: 357–
　　　　367, 1954.

69. *Achras Zapota* L., Sp. Pl. 1,190, 1753.

A. Zapota β Achras Zapotilla Jacq., Select. Stirp. Am. Hist.
　　57, pl. 41, 1763.

Sapota Achras Mill., Gard. Dict., ed. 8, Sapota No. 1, 1768.

Achras zapotilla (Jacq.) Nutt., N. Am. Sylva 3: 28, 1849.

Manilkara zapotilla (Jacq.) Gilly, Yale Univ. School For.
　　Trop. Woods 73: 20, 1943.

　　See Lam, Trav. Bot. Néerl., Rec. 36: 509–525, 1939;
　　　　Baehni, Candollea 9: 147–476, 1942;
　　　　Gilly, Trop. Woods, 73: 1–22, 1943;
　　　　Cronquist, Lloydia 9: 241–292, 1946;
　　　　Lawrence, Gent. Herb. 8: 61, 1949;
　　　　Monachino, Phytologia 4: 94–118, 1952;
　　　　Little, U. S. Dept. Agric., Agric. Handbook 41: 43–44,
　　　　1953.

70. Aspergillus [Micheli] ex Fries, Syst. Mycol. 3: 383–385,
　　1829.

Eurotium Link ex Fries, Syst. Mycol. 3: 331, 1832.

　　See Fisher, in Engler & Prantl, Natürl. Pflanzenfam. 1(1):
　　　　52, 58, 301–304, 1896.

　　Thom & Raper, Man. Aspergilli 1945.

71. *Cyrtophyllum ? lanceolatum* A. DC., Prodr. 9 : 31, 1845.

72. *Pinus ball* Brown, U. S. Geol. Surv., Prof. Pap. 185: 53, pl.
　　8, fig. 5, 1934.

P. balli Brown emend. Brown, Wash. Acad. Sci., Jour. 30:
　　354, 1940.

　　See Lamotte, Geol. Soc. Am., Mem. 51: 253, 1952.

73. *Rollandia lanceolata* Gaud., Bot. Voy. Freyc. Uranie 458,
(1830) = [1829]; Atlas, pl. 74 (as R. montana), 1826.

Lobelia lanceolata (Gaud.) Endl., Wien Mus. Naturgesch.,
Ann. 1: 170, 1836.

R. lanceolata Gaud. var. *grandifolia* DC., Prodr. 7: 344,
1838.

R. lanceolata Gaud. var. *typica* Rock, Bishop Mus., Mem.
7(2): 371-373, pl. 209, 1919.

R. lanceolata Gaud. var. *Rockii* St. John & Hosaka, Bishop
Mus., Occ. Pap. 11: 13, 1935.

See Fosberg, Am. Jour. Bot. 26: 229, 1939;
St. John, Bishop Mus., Occ. Pap. 15: 236, 1940.

74. *Fraxinus pubescens* Lam. δ *subpubescens* (Pers.) Pursh, Fl.
Am. Sept. 1: 9, 1814.

F. pubescens* subpubescens Pers., Syn. Pl. 2: 605, 1807.

F. juglandifolia Lam. β *subintegerrima* Vahl, Enum. Pl. 1:
50-51, 1804.

F. lanceolata Borkh., Handb. Forstbot. Forsttechn. 1: 826-
827, 1800.

F. caroliniana Mill. β *F. latifolia* Willd., Sp. Pl. of L., ed.
4 by Willd. 4: 1,103, 1806.

F. expansa Willd., Berl. Baumzucht, ed. 2, 150, 1811.

F. viridis Michx., Hist. Arb. For. Am. Sept. 3: 115-117, pl.
10, 1813.

F. pennsylvanica Marsh. var. *lanceolata* (Borkh.) Sarg., Silva
6: 50-51, pl. 122, 1894.

F. pennsylvanica Marsh. var. *subintegerrima* (Vahl) Fern.,
Rhodora 49: 159, 1947.

75. *Aira* L., Gen. Pl., ed. 5, 31, 1754.

Aspris Adans., Fam. Pl. 2: 496, 522, 1763.

Deschampsia Beauv., Agrost. 91, pl. 8, fig. 3, 1812.

See Hitchcock, U. S. Dept. Agric., Bul. 772: 114-116,
1920.

76. *Clerodendron aculeatum* (L.) *Griseb.* var. *gracile* Griseb. &
Moldenke, in Moldenke, Geogr. Distrib. Verbenac. 5-7,
14, 36, 1939.

Clerodendrum aculeatum (L.) Schlecht. var. *gracile* Griseb. &
Moldenke, in Moldenke, Geogr. Distrib. Verbenac. 29,
43, 46, 47, 158, 180, 1939.

Clerodendrum aculeatum (L.) Schlecht. var. *gracile* Griseb. &
Moldenke ex Moldenke, Some New Species and Vars.
Verbenac. 13, n.d. [1940].

77. *Passiflora edulis* Sims var. *flavicarpa* C. D. Miller, Bazore &
Robbins, Hawaii Agric. Exp. Sta., Bul. 77: 66, fig. 9,
1934.
P. edulis Sims forma *flavicarpa* Degener, Fl. Haw. 250:
7/30/'32.
P. edulis flavicarpa W. T. Pope, Hawaii Agric. Exp. Sta.,
Bul. 74: 13, 1935.
P. edulis Sims var. *flavicarpa* C. D. Miller & Bazore, Hawaii
Agric. Exp. Sta., Bul. 96: 97, fig. 14, 1945.

78. *Mentha gentilis* L., Sp. Pl. 577, 1753.
Mentha arvensis × viridis F. W. Schultz, Pollichia, Jahresber.
12: 42, 1854.
M. Wirtgeniana F. W. Schultz, Pollichia, Jahresber. 12: 41,
1854.

79. *Pfeifferago* Ktze., Rev. Gen. Pl. 1: 227, 1891.
Codia J. R. & G. Forst., Char. Gen. 59–60, pl. 30, 1776.

80. *Caladium* Vent. in Roem., Arch. Bot. 2: 347–351, 1800.
Calladium acre R. Br., Prodr. Fl. Nov. Holl. 336, (1799) =
[1810].
Colocasia esculenta (L.) Schott in Schott & Endl. var. *acris*
(R. Br.) A. F. Hill, Harvard Univ. Bot. Mus. Leafl. 7:
117, 1939.
Colocasia acris (R. Br.) Schott in Schott & Endl., Melet. Bot.
1: 18, 1832.

81. *Anemone quinquefolia* L. var. *interior* Fern., Rhodora 37: 260,
1935.
A. quinquefolia L. var. *bifolia* Farw., Mich. Acad. Sci. Arts
Lett., Pap. 1: 94, 1923.

82. *Platyschkuhria* (Gray) Rydb., Torrey Bot. Club, Bul. 33: 154,
1906.
Cordylophorum Rydb., Fl. Rocky Mts., 590, 1,064, (1917) =
[1918].
Pycnosphace Rydb., Fl. Rocky Mts., 747, 1,066, (1917) =
[1918].

83. *Gymnobythus* (A. DC.) Gray, Am. Acad. Arts Sci., Proc. 10: 321, 1875.

Gymnobythus A. DC., in DC., Prodr. 9: 296, 1845.

84. *Anonymos* (Lupino affinis) *rotundifolia* Walt., Fl. Carol. 181, 1788.

Crotalaria rotundifolia Poir. in Lam., Encyc. Méth. Bot. Suppl. 2: 402, (1811) = [1812].

See Fernald & Schubert, Rhodora 50: 202–203, 1948.

85. *Abrotanum* Tourn., Inst. Rei Herb. 1: 459, 1700.

Abrotanum L., Syst. Nat., ed. 1, 1735; repr. in Jour. Bot. Brit. For. 38: 440, 1900.

Artemisia L. sect. *Abrotanum* (Necker) Bess., Soc. Nat. Mosc., Nov. Mem. 3: 21, 1834.

Euartemisia Gray, Syn. Fl. N. Am. 1(2): 369, 1884.

See Hall & Clements, Carnegie Inst. Wash., Publ. 326: 46, 49, 1923.

86. *Lobelia glandulosa* Walt. γ *obtusifolia* DC., Prodr. 7: 378, 1839.

L. Puberula Michx. var. α *glabella* Elliott, Sketch Bot. S. Carol. 1: 267, (1821) = [1817].

L. puberula Michx. β *glabella* Hook., Curtis's Bot. Mag. 61: pl. 3,292, 1834.

L. puberula Michx. var. *obtusifolia* (A. DC.) Fern., Rhodora 49: 184, 1947.

87. *Cyrtandra triflora* Gaud. β var. *grandifolia* Hbd., Fl. Haw. Is. 332, 1888.

C. grandifolia Elmer, Leafl. Philipp. Bot. 7: 2,663, 1915.

C. laxiflora Mann var. *grandifolia* (Hbd.) Rock, Am. Jour. Bot. 6: 207–208, 1919.

C. laxiflora Mann var. *rhizantha* Rock, Am. Jour. Bot. 6: 207, 1919.

C. rhizantha Kränzlin, Linn. Soc. Lond. Bot., Jour. 37: 277, 1906.

C. stupantha St. John & Storey, Bishop Mus., Occ. Pap. 20: 88, 1950.

88. *Delphinium Nuttallii* Gray, Bot. Gaz. 12: 51, 54, 1887.

D. Nuttallianum Pritz. ex Walpers, Repert. Bot. Syst. 2: Suppl. 1: 744, 1843.

89. *Dryopteris Linnaeana* C. Chr., Ind. Fil. 275, 1906.

Polypodium Dryopteris L., Sp. Pl. 1,093, 1753.

Polystichum Dryopteris (L.) Roth ex Mertens, Röm. Arch.
Bot. 2(1): 106, 1799.

Polystichum Dryopteris (L.) Roth, Tent. Fl. Germ. 3(1): 80–
82, 1800.

Nephrodium Dryopteris (L.) Michx., Fl. Bor.-Am. 2: 270,
1803.

Filix pumila Gilib., Exer. Phytol. 2: 558, 1792.

Polypodium pulchellum Salisb., Prodr. Stirp. Hort. Allerton
404, 1796.

Lastraea Dryopteris (L.) Bory, in Dict. Class. 9: 233, 1826.

Aspidium Dryopteris (L.) Baumg., Enum. Stirp. Transsil. 4:
29, 1846.

Phegopteris Dryopteris (L.) Fée, Gen. Fil. (Mem. Foug. 5:)
243, 1850–1852.

Phegopteris Dryopteris (L.) Fée *disjuncta* Trel., Harrim.
Alaska Exped. 5: 382, 1904.

Gymnocarpium Dryopteris (L.) Newm., Phytol. 4: 371, 1851.

Dryopteris pulchella (Salisb.) Hayek, Fl. Steiermark 1: 39,
1908.

Thelypteris Dryopteris (L.) Slosson in Rydb., Fl. Rocky
Mts. 1,044, 1,069, 1917.

Dryopteris triangularis (St. Lager) Herter, Herb. Boiss., Bul.
II, 8: 797, 1908.

Dryopteris disjuncta (Rupr.) C. V. Morton, Rhodora 43: 217,
1941.

Polypodium Dryopteris L. γ *P. disjunctum* Rupr., Distr. Cr.
Vasc. Ross. 52, 1845; Pflanzenk. Russ. Reich, Beitr. 3:
52, 1845.

Polypodium disjunctum Rupr. ex Schur, Oestr. Bot. Zeitschr.
8: 193, 1858.

Polypodium Dryopteris L. γ *disjunctum* (Rupr.) Ledeb., Fl.
Ross. 4: 509, 1853.

Dryopteris Linnaeana C. Chr. var. *disjuncta* (Rupr.) Fomin,
Fl. Siberia et Orient Extr. 79, 1930.

Gymnocarpium Dryopteris (L.) Newm. var. *disjunctum* (Rupr.)
Ching, Biol. Lab., Sci. Soc. China, Bot. Ser., Contr. 9:
41, 1933.

90. *Rubus Grimesii* Bailey, Gent. Herb. 2: 331, fig. 158, 1932; 5: 406, fig. 184, 1943; 7: 494–495, 1949.
See Fernald, Rhodora 50: 79, 1948.

91. *Charpentiera obovata* Gaud., Bot. Voy. Freyc. Uranie 444, (1826) =[1829]; Alt. 500–600 hexap.
Viburnum nudum L. var. *angustifolium* T. & G. See Fernald, Rhodora 49: 93, 1947, flowering but only 3 or 4 feet high, . . .
Paspalum setaceum Michx. var. *calvescens* Fern., Rhodora 49: 121, 1947, about 1/2 mile west of Kilby, Virginia.

92. *Diellia Brownii* E. Br., Bishop Mus., Bul. 89: 46, 1931.

93. *Argyroxiphium sandwicense* DC. See Hbd., Fl. Haw. Is. 219, 1888, Ahinahina.

94. *Vrydagzynea* Bl., Coll. Orch. Archip. Ind. 71–72, pl. 17 E-F; 19, fig. 2–3; 20, fig. 1–4, 1858.

95. *Nama Sandwicensis* Gray, Am. Acad. Arts Sci., Proc. 5: 338, 1861.
N. sandvicense Gray emend. Brand, in Engler, Pflanzenreich IV, fam. 251: 152, 1913.
See C. L. Hitchcock, Am. Jour. Bot. 20: 415–534, 1933.

96. *Durio* Adans., Fam. Pl. 2: 399, 1763.

97. *Geniostoma* J. R. & G. Forst., Char. Gen. 23–24, pl. 12, 1776.

98. *Polypodium* L., Gen. Pl., ed. 5, 485, 1754; Sp. Pl. 1,082–1,094, 1753.
Polypodium L. emend. C. Chr., Ind. Fil. 506–575, 1906.
Polypodium L. emend. Copel., Gen. Fil. 180–181, 1947.

99. *Heteropogon* Pers., Syn. Pl. 2: 533, 1807.

100. *Artocarpus* J. R. & G. Forst., Char. Gen. Pl. Mar. Austral. 101–102, pl. 51, 51a, 1776.
Artocarpus Forst. f., Fl. Ins. Austral. Prodr. 64, 1786.
Radermachia Thunb., Vet. Akad. Stockh., Handl. 37: 250–255, 1776.

101. *Oryzopsis* Michx., Fl. Bor.-Am. 1: 51, pl. 9, 1803.

102. *Solanum vulgare* L., Sp. Pl. 186, 1753.
S. vulgare Hegetschw., ed. Heer, Fl. Schweiz, 219, 1840.

103. *Rhus Coriaria* L., Sp. Pl. 265, 1753.
R. javanica L., Sp. Pl. 265, 1753.
R. angustifolium L., Sp. Pl. 267, 1753.
R. radicans L., Sp. Pl. 266, 1753.
R. Toxicodendr L., Sp. Pl. 266, 1753.
R. Copallinum L., Sp. Pl. 266, 1753.

104. *Salix Hippophaefolia* Thuill., Fl. Env. Paris, ed. 2, 514–515, (An VII) = [1799].

105. *Elaeagnus argenteus* Nutt., Fraser's Cat. 1813; repr. Pittonia 2: 117, 1890.
E. argentea Moench, Meth. Pl. Hort. Marburg 638, 1794.
Elaeagrus argentea Pursh, Fl. Am. Sept. 114, 1814.
Elaeagnus argentea Colla, Hort. Ripul., pl. 28, 1824.
E. commutata Bernh., Allg. Thuer, Gartenz. 2: 137, 1843.
Elaeagrus Pallas, Fl. Ross. 1(1): 10–11, pl. 4–5, 1784.
See Shinners, Rhodora 57: 290–293, 1955;
Graustein, Rhodora 58: 20–22, 1956;
Cronquist *et al.*, Rhodora 58: 23–24, 1956; 58: 281–289, 1956.
Cronquist, Rhodora 59: 100, 1957.

106. *Rosa lapwaiensis* St. John, Fl. S. E. Wash. & Adj. Ida. 208–209, 1937.

107. *Carex chlorocystis* Böck. in Engl. Bot. Jahrb. 5: 520, 1884.

108. *Cardamine Matthioli* Moretti ex Comol., Fl. Com. 5: 157–159, 1847.

109. *Eleocharis* R. Br., Prodr. Fl. Nov. Holl. 224, 1810.
Heleocharis R. Br. emend. Lestib., Essai Cypérac. 22, 41, 1819.

110. *Carex Mühlenbergii* Willd., Sp. Pl. of L., ed. 4 by Willd., 4: 231, 1805.
C. Muhlenbergii Schk. sensu Brongn., Voy. Duperr. Bot. 2: 151, 1829.
C. Muhlenbergii Kunth ex Boott, Ill. Gen. Carex 3: 125, 1862.

111. *Micranthemum* Michx., Fl. Bor.-Am. 1: 10, pl. 2, 1803.

112. *Brosimum parinarioides* Ducke, Jard. Bot. Rio de Janeiro, Arch. 3: 23–30, 1922.

113. *Aecidium Gaurae* Ellis & Everh., Erythea 1: 205, 1893.

114. *Carex chlorantha* R. Br., Prodr. Fl. Nov. Holl. 242, 1810.

115. *Psychotria Taupotinii* F. Br., Bishop Mus., Bul. 130: 313-
315, fig. 54, 1935.

116. *Gaura mollis* Nutt. ex. T. & G., Fl. N. Am. 1: 519, 1840.

117. Seemann, B., Fl. Vit. 1-453, 100 pl., 1865-1873.

118. *Aplopappus* Cass., Dict. Sci. Nat. 56: 168-170, 1828.
Haplopappus Cass. ex Endl., Gen. Pl. 385-386, (1840) =
[1837].
Diplopappus Less., Soc. Philom., Bul. Sci. 1817: 137, 1817.

119. Wawra, H., Beiträge zur Flora der Hawai'schen Inseln 1-
158, n. d.

120. *Stellandria* Brickell, Med. Repos. New York 6: 327, 1803.

121. *Pinus Murrayana* Oregon Committee, Bot. Exped. Oreg.
[Rept. 8:] 2, No. 740, pl. [4], [1853].
See Murray, Edinb. Bot. Soc., Trans. 6: (225) 350, 1860.
Little, Am. Jour. Bot. 31: 588-590, 1944.

122. *Gilia (Dactylophyllum) Parryae* Gray, Am. Acad. Arts Sci.,
Proc. 12: 76-78, 1876.

123. *Hyssopus* [Tourn.] ex L., Gen. Pl., ed. 5, 248, 1754.

124. *Bebbia* Greene, Calif. Acad. Sci., Bul. 1: 179, 1885.
Kuhnioides Gray, Syn. Fl. N. Am. 1(2): 113, 1884.

125. *Harrimanella* Cov., Wash. Acad. Sci., Proc. 3: 570, 574-
576, fig. 62, 1901.
Andromeda L., Gen. Pl., ed. 5, 186, 1754.

126. *Canavalia pubescens* H. & A., Bot. Beechey Voy. 81, 1832.
C. galeata Gaud. var. *pubescens* (H. & A.) Gray, Bot. U. S.
Expl. Exped. 15(1): 441, 1854.
C. galeata (Gaud.) H. & A. var. *pubescens* (H. & A.) St.
John, Bishop Mus., Occ. Pap. 15(22): 231-233, 1940.

127. *Kosteletzkya* Presl, Rel. Haenk. 2: 130, pl. 70, (1831) =
[1835].

128. *Railliardia* Gaud., Bot. Voy. Freyc. Uranie 469, (1826) =
[1830].
Raillardia Gaud., Bot. Voy. Freyc. Uranie Atlas, pl. 83,
1826.

Dubautia Gaud., Bot. Voy. Freyc. Uranie 469, (1826) =
    [1830]; Atlas, pl. 84, 1826.
    See Keck, Bishop Mus., Occ. Pap. 11(19): 24–28, 1936.

129. *Crypsinus* Presl, Epim. Bot. 123, 1849. See Copel., Gen.
    Fil. 205, 1947.
    Microterus Presl, Epim. Bot. 124, 1849.
    Phymatopsis J. Sm., Hist. Fil. 104, 1875.

130. *Penaea* L., Gen. Pl., ed. 5, 50, 1754.

131. *Amsinckia Lemmonii* Macbr., Gray Herb., Contr. n.s. 48:
    50–51, 1916.

132. *Chrysothamnus* (Nutt.) Gray, Am. Acad. Arts Sci., Proc. 8:
    642, 1873.
    Chrysothamnus Nutt., Am. Phil. Soc., Trans. II, 7: 323,
    1841.

133. *Brassia* R. Br. in Ait., Hort. Kew., ed. 2, 5: 215, 1813.

134. *Bamia Manihot* (L.) R. Br. ex Sims, Curtis's Bot. Mag. 41:
    pl. 1,702, 1815.
    B. Manihot (L.) Wall., Cat. (Numer. List Pl. E. Ind.), No.
    1,926, 1829.
    Bamia [L.] R. Br. ex Wall., Pl. Asiat. Rar. 1: 39, 1830.
    Bammia Rupp., Fl. Ienensis 31, 1726; and ed. Haller, 39–40,
    1745.

135. *Monophyllaea* R. Br. in Benn. Pl. Jav. Rar. 121, 1838–1852.

136. *Euptelea* Sieb. & Zucc., Fl. Jap. 1: 133, pl. 72, 1835.

137. *Pinus resinosa* Ait., Hort. Kew. 3: 367, 1789.

138. *Cocos nucifera* L., Sp. Pl. 1,188, 1753.

139. *Oxytropis johannensis* (Fern.) Fern., Rhodora 30: 145, 1928.
    O. campestris (L.) DC. var. *johannensis* Fern., Rhodora 1:
    88, 1899.
    Carex katahdinensis Fern., Rhodora 3: 171, 1901.
    Melica Nebrodensis Parl., Giorn. Bot. Ital. 2(1): 198, 1844.

140. *Aster pseudo-Asa-Grayi* Makino, Jour. Jap. Bot. 8(2): 14,
    1932; Hara, Enum. Sperm. Jap. 2: 135, 1952.
    Aster Asa-Grayi Makino, Bot. Mag. Tokyo 22: 157, 1908.

141. *Panicum ciliatiflorum* Wood, Class-book 2: 786, 1861.
    P. ciliatifolium Kunth, Distrib. Meth. Gram. 1: 36, (1835) =
    [1829].

142. *Betula coerulea* Blanchard, Betula 1: one page, unnumbered, 1904.

    B. × *caerulea* Blanchard (pro specie), Little, Check List Nat. Trees U. S., For. Serv., U. S. Dept. Agric. 30, 1944.

143. *Anaphalis margaritacea* (L.) B. & H., Gen. Pl. 2: 303, 1873.

    Gnaphalium margaritaceum L., Sp. Pl. 850, 1753.

    Antennaria margaritacea (L.) R. Br., Linn. Soc. Lond., Trans. 12: 123, 1817.

    Anaphalis margaritacea (L.) Benth. ex C. B. Clarke, Compos. Indicae 103, 1876.

    Anaphalis margaritacea (L.) C. B. Clarke in Hook. f., Fl. Brit. Ind. 3: 282, 1881.

144. *Baileya* Kuetz., Tab. Phyc. 7: 35, pl. 87, fig. 3, 1857, non Harv. & Gray in Torr. (1848).

145. *Polypodium vulgare* Auct. east. Am., non L., Sp. Pl. 1,085, 1753.

    P. virginianum L., Sp. Pl. 1,085, 1753.

    See Fernald, Rhodora 24: 125–142, 1922.

146. *Zingiber* Boehm. in Ludw., Def. Gen. Pl., ed. 3 by Boehm. 89, 1760.

    Zingiber Mill., Gard. Dict., abridg. ed. 4, 3: under letter Z, 1754.

    Zinziber P. Browne, Civ. Nat. Hist. Jamaica 119, 1756.

    Zingiber Adans., Fam. Pl. 2: 66, 1763.

    Dymczewiczia Horan., Prodr. Scitam. 26, 1862.

    Lampujang Koen., in Retz., Obs. Bot. 3: 62, 1783.

    Zerumbet Lestib., Ann. Sci. Nat. Bot. II, 15: 329–331, pl. 21, fig. 13–17, 1841.

147. *Parnassia Turczaninowii* Ledeb., Fl. Ross. 1: 263, 1842.

148. *Asplenium platyneuron* (L.) Oakes in Eaton, Ferns N. Am. 1: 24, 1878.

    Acrostichum platyneuros L., Sp. Pl. 1,069, 1753.

    See Fernald, Rhodora 37: 382–384, 1935.

149. *Palmocarpon* Lesquereux, U. S. Geol. Surv., Terr. Rept. 7: 119, 1878.

    P. compositum (Lesq.) Lesq., U. S. Geol. Surv., Terr. Rept. 7: 119, pl. 11, fig. 4, 1878.

Carpolithes compositus Lesq., U. S. Geol. Surv. Terr., Fifth Ann. Rept. for 1871: Suppl. 16–17, 1872.

150. *Asplenium* × *Souchei* R. de Litard., Soc. Bot. Deux-Sèvres, Bul. 21: 100, pl. 1, 1910.

151. *Muscites* Brongn., Hist. Vég. Fossiles 93, pl. 10, fig. 1–2, 1828.

Muscites florissanti (Knowlton) Steere, Am. Midl. Nat. 36: 310, 1947.

Polytrichum (?) *florissanti* Knowlton, U. S. Natl. Mus., Proc. 51: 245, pl. 12, fig. 4, 1916.

152. *Pyrus hybrida* Moench, Verz. Ausland. Bäume u. Stauden 90, pl. 6, 1785.

Aronia hybrida (Moench) Zabel in Beissner, Schelle & Zabel, Handb. Laubholz-Benennung 193, 1903.

× *Sorbaronia* Schneid., Fedde Repert. Sp. Nov. 3: 134, 1906.

× *Sorbaronia monstrosa* (Zabel) C. Schneid., Fedde Repert. Sp. Nov. 3: 134, 1906.

Aronia monstrosa (Hort.) Zabel in Beissner, Schelle & Zabel, Handb. Laubholz-Benennung 677, 1903.

153. *Cactus ferox* Nutt. in Fraser's Cat. 1813; repr. in Pittonia 2: 116, 1890.

C. ferox Nutt., Gen. N. Am. Pl. 1: 296, 1818.

Opuntia missouriensis DC., Prodr. 3: 472, 1828.

C. ferox Willd., Enum. Pl. Hort. Berol., ed. Schlecht., Suppl. 35, 1813.

Opuntia polyacantha Haw., Suppl. Pl. Succ. 82, 1819.

Mammillaria Haw., Syn. Pl. Succ. 177, 1812.

Cactus L., Gen. Pl., ed. 5, 210, 1754; Sp. Pl. 466–470, 1753.

See Britton & Rose, Carnegie Inst. Wash., Publ. 248(1): 199, 1919;

Shinners, Rhodora 57: 290–293, 1955;

Graustein, Rhodora 58: 20–22, 1956;

Cronquist *et al.*, Rhodora 58: 23–24, 1956;

Shinners, Rhodora 58: 281–289, 1956;

Cronquist, Rhodora 59: 100, 1957.

154. *Delissea Kunthiana* Gaud., Voy. Freyc. Bonite, Atlas, pl. 77, 1844.

Cyanea Kunthiana Hbd., Fl. Haw. Is. 264, 1888.
Cyanea Bonita Rock, Bishop Mus., Mem. 7(2): 51, 1919.
C. Bishopii Rock, Bishop Mus., Mem. 7(2): 277–279, pl.
    52, 155, 1919.

155. Sm. =Smith, Sir James Edward (1759–1828). Consider
    abbreviations for Albert Charles (1906–   ); Annie
    Lorrain (1854–1937); Arlow Irving (1911–   ); Erwin
    Frink (1854–1927); Gilbert Morgan (1885–   ); Jared
    Gage (1866–1957); Johannes Jacobus (1867–1947); John
    (1798–1888); John Donnell (1829–1928); Karl August
    Harald (Harry) (1889–   ); Lyman Bradford (1904–
    ); William (1808–1857); Sir William Wright
    (1875–1956).

156. *Elymotrigia* Hyl., Bot. Notis. 358, 1953.

157. F. Muell. =Sir Ferdinand Jacob Heinrich von Mueller (1825–
    1896). Consider abbreviations for Carl (1817–1870); Carl
    Alfred Ernst (1855–1907); Ferdinand (another publishing in
    1852–1862); Franz (publishing 1829–1859); Jean (1828–
    1896); Jean Baptista (1806–1894); Johann Karl August
    (1818–1899); Johann Sebastian (later John) (1715?–1790?);
    Joseph (published from 1832–1859); Otto Frederik (1730–
    1784); Philipp Jakob (1832–1889).
    See Eardley, Australasian Herb. News 12: 3–4, 1953.

158. *Dicranum (Scopario-Dicranum) yakushimense* Sak., Jour.
    Jap. Bot. 27: 155, 1952.

159. *Nothofagus* Bl., Mus. Bot. Lugd.-Bat. 1: 307, 1850.
    Fagaster Spach, Hist. Nat. Vég. Phan. 11: 142, 1842.
    Calucechinus Hombr. & Jacq. in Dumont d'Urville, Voy.
        Pol Sud Astrolabe Zélée Bot. Atlas, Dicot. 19, pl. 6,
        7 Σ, 1844; 8 π 60, 1845.
    Calusparassus Hombr. & Jacq. in Dumont d'Urville, Voy.
        Pol Sud Astrolabe Zélée Bot. Atlas Dicot., pl. 6 Σ,
        1844; pl. 7 Γ, 1844; 8 Ψ, 1845.

160. *Nomosa* I. M. Johnston, Jour. Arn. Arb. 35: 24–27, 1954.

161. *Gnaphalium sandwicensium* Gaud., Bot. Voy. Freyc. Uranie
        466, (1826) =[1830].
    G. sandwicensium Gaud. var. *typicum* Sherff forma *canum*
        Sherff, Am. Jour. Bot. 36: 504, 1949.

G. sandwicensium Gaud. var. *typicum* Sherff forma *olivaceum* Sherff, Am. Jour. Bot. 36: 504, 1949.

162. *Alcicornium* Gaud., Bot. Voy. Freyc. Uranie 48, 1826.
Platycerium Desv., Linn. Soc. Paris, Mém. 6(2): 213, 1827.

163. *Gerbera* (*viridifolia* var.?) *Conrathii* Thell. spec. vel var. nov., Naturf. Gesell. Zürich, Vierteljahrschr. 68: 454, 1923.

164. *Trematosphaeriopsis* Elenkin, Jard. Bot. St. Petersb., Bul. 136–146, 1901.
Trematosphaeris Clements, Gen. Fungi 35, 1909.

165. *Aecidium Violae* Schum., Enum. Pl. Saell. 2: 224, 1803.
Uredo Violae Schum., Enum. Pl. Saell. 2: 233, 1803.
Puccinia violae DC., Fl. Fr. 6: 62, 1815.
P. densa Diet. & Holw. in Dietel, Hedwigia 36: 298, 1897.
Dicaeoma Violae (DC.) Ktze., Rev. Gen. Pl. 3(3): 471, 1898.
Puccinia violae (Schum.) DC. ex Arthur, J. C., Man. Rusts U. S. & Can. 311, 1934.

166. *Fraxinus juglandifolia* Lam., Encyc. Méth. Bot. 2: 548, (1786) =[1788].
F. americana L. *juglandifolia* D. J. Browne, Trees Am. 398, 1846.
F. americana L. var. *juglandifolia* [Lam.] D. J. Browne ex Rehder, Bibliog. Cult. Trees & Shrubs 557, 1949.

167. *Arachis hypogaea* L. var. *microcarpa* A. Chevalier, Rev. de Bot. Appl. et Agr. Trop. 9: 193, pl. 5, fig. 3; pl. 6, fig. 5, 1929.
A. hypogaea L. forma *microcarpa* (A. Chev.) Hermann, U. S. Dept. Agric., Monogr. 19: 14, 1954.

168. *Lipotriche* sensu Less., Syn. Gen. Composit. 231, 1832; Linnaea 6: 510, 1831.
Lipotriche R. Br., Linn. Soc. Lond., Trans. 12: 118, 1817.
Lipochaeta DC., Prodr. 5: 610, 1836.
Microchaeta Nutt., Am. Phil. Soc., Trans. II, 7: 450–452, 1841.
Schizophyllum Nutt., Am. Phil. Soc., Trans. II, 7: 452–453, 1841.
See Sherff, Bishop Mus., Bul. 135: 24, 1935.
Silva, Univ. Calif., Publ. Bot. 25: 281, 1952.

169. *Nicandra physaloides* (L.) Gaertn., Fruct. 2: 237-238, pl. 131, fig. 2, (1802) = [1791].

Atropa physalodes L., Sp. Pl. 181, 1753.

Physalodes peruvianum Ktze., Rev. Gen. Pl. 452, 1891.

Nicandra Physalodes (L.) Pers. ex Robins. & Fern., in Gray's Man., ed. 7, 716, 1908.

Physalodes Boehm., ed. of Ludw. Def. Gen. Pl. 41-42, 1760.

Physaloides Moench, Meth. Pl. Hort. Bot. Marburg. 473, 1794.

Pentagonia physalodes (L.) Hiern, Cat. Welw. Afr. Pl. 1: 752, 1898.

Physalodes physalodes (L.) Britton, Torrey Bot. Club, Mem. 5: 287, 1894.

170. Viguier, R. (†), issued by Meslin, R., Les Legumineuses de Madagascar. Archives de Botanique 6: 1-823, 1944. There were printed 500 copies, of which 498 were destroyed while still in the printing house in the Battle of Paris, 1944. Two copies now exist, one with M. Meslin, one in the Museum National d'Histoire Naturelle, Paris. The book contains numerous new species.

171. *Teucrium cubense* Jacq. ssp. *depressum* (Small) McClintock & Epling, Brittonia 5: 505, 1946, Sept. 6.

T. depressum Small, New York Bot. Gard., Bul. 1: 288, 1899.

T. cubense Jacq. var. *densum* Jepson, Man. Fl. Pl. Calif. 861, 1925, Sept. 23 ?

See L. C. Wheeler, Am. Jour. Bot. 29: 19s, 1942, Dec.

172. *Angervilla* Neck., Elem. Bot. 1: 351, 1790.

Matourea Aublet, Hist. Pl. Guiane 2: 641-643, 1775; 4: pl. 259, 1775.

Stemodia L., Syst. Veg., ed. 10, 1,118, 1759.

173. *Pandanus aimiriikensis* Martelli in Kanehira, Fl. Micrones. 60, fig. 1, 1933; Kyushu Imp. Univ., Dept. Agric., Jour. 4(6): 259, 1935, nom. seminud.; Bot. Mag. Tokyo 48: 125, fig. 7, 1934.

174. *Fagaster Dombeyi* (Mirb.) Spach, Hist. Nat. Vég. Phan. 11: 142, 1842.

175. *Triticum strictum* Detharding, Consp. Pl. Magn. Megap. 11,
    1828.
    Agropyrum strictum (Dethard.) Reichb., Fl. Germ. Excurs.
        21, 1830.
    Triticum elymogenes Arndt, Flora 42: 215, 1859.
    Triticum junceum × *Hordeum* (*Elymus*) *arenarium* Marsson,
        Fl. Neuvorp. u. Rügen 598, 1869.
    Triticum junceum × *Elymus arenarius* Nyman ex Aschers. &
        Graebn., Syn. Mitteleur. Fl. 2(1): 748, 1902.
    × *Tritordeum strictum* Asch. & Graebn., Syn. Mitteleur. Fl.
        2: 748, 1902.
    Agropyrum junceum × *Elymus arenarius* G. Camus, Mus.
        Natl. Hist. Nat. Paris, Bul. 6: 538, 1927.
    × *Agroelymus strictus* (Reichb.) G. Camus in A. Camus,
        Mus. Natl. Hist. Nat. Paris, Bul. 6: 538, 1927.
    × *Agroelymus strictus* (Dethard.) G. Camus ex Rousseau,
        Jard. Bot. Montreal, Mem. 29: 14, 1952.
176. *Agropsammelymus* Lepage, Nat. Canad. 80: 196, 1953.
177. × *Agroelymus Adamsii* Rousseau n.m. *jamesensis* Lepage,
        Nat. Canad. 80: 197, 1953.
    × *Agroelymus jamesensis* Lepage, Nat. Canad. 79: 245–246,
        1952.
178. *Acer saccharum* Marsh cl. 'Newton Sentry' B. Harkness,
        Baileya 2: 99–101, fig. 31B, 1954.
    A. saccharinum columnare Temple, Temple's Cat. 1887.
179. *Equisetum sylvaticum* L. var. *pauciramosum* Milde forma
        neoserotinum Victorin, Univ. Montréal. Lab. Bot.,
        Contr. 9: 120, 1927.
    See Boivin, Can. Field Nat. 63: 75, 1949.
180. *Juggerlandia mucida* (Schulzer) McGinty ex Lloyd, Mycol.
        Writ. 7: 1,230–1,231, pl. 259, fig. 2,570, 1923.
    J. mucida (Schulzer) Lloyd teste Stevenson & Cash, Lloyd
        Libr. & Mus., Bul. 35 (Mycol., Ser.8): 26, 1936.
181. *Eragrostis perplexa* L. H. Harvey, Univ. Microfilms, Publ.
        967: 1948; Torrey Bot. Club, Bul. 81: 409–410, 1954.
182. × *Tsugo-Piceo-Tsuga Jeffreyi* (Henry) Campo-Duplan &
        Gaussen, Lab. For. Toulouse, Trav. I, 4(24): 11, 1948.
    Tsuga Jeffreyi (Henry) Henry, Roy. Irish Acad., Proc.
        35B(4): 55, 1919.

Tsuga Pattoniana Engelm. var. *Jeffreyi* Henry in Elwes &
  Henry, Trees Gr. Brit. & Irel. 2: 231, 1907.

183. *Culhamia* Forsk., Fl. Aegypt.-Arab. 96, 1775.

184. *Juglandicarya integrifoliolata* (Kuang) Hu, Paleobot. 1: 264,
  1952.

Carya sinensis Dode, Soc. Dendrol. France, Bul. 24: 61,
  1912.

Annamocarya indochinensis Cheval., Intern. Bot. Appl.,
  Rev. 21: 504, 1941.

Juglans indochinensis Cheval., Intern. Bot. Appl., Rev. 21:
  504, 1941.

Rhamphocarya integrifoliolata Kuang, Icon. Flor. Sinicae 1:
  1-2, pl. 1, 1941.

Annamocarya sinensis (Dode) Leroy, Intern. Bot. Appl.,
  Rev. 30: 426, 1950; Açad. Sci. Paris, Compt. Rend.
  232: 432-434, 1,007-1,009, 1951.

  See Scott, Am. Jour. Bot. 40: 666-669, 1953.

185. *Bryum argenteum* L., Sp. Pl. 1,120, 1753.

B. argenteum L. ex Hedw., Sp. Musc. 181, 1801.

186. *Fucus* Theophrastus, Peri Phuton Historia 4: 6-2; 4: 6-9;
  Inquiry into Plants, ed. A. Hort 1: 328, 334, 1916.

Fucus Tourn., Inst. Rei Herb. 1: 565-569; 3: pl. 334-336,
  1700.

Fucus S. F. Gray, Nat. Arr. Brit. Pl. 1: 389, 1821.

Muscus marinus C. Bauhin, Pinax 363-364, 1671.

187. *Dendrophthoë* Mart., Flora 13(1): 109, 1830.

Dendrophtoe pentandra (L.) Miq., Fl. Ind. Bat. 1(1): 818,
  (1855) = [1858].

Loranthus pentandrus L., Mant. 1: 63, 1767.

L. pentandrus sensu Heyne ex R. & S., in Syst. Veg. of
  Linnaeus, ed. nov. by R. & S., 7: 112, 1829.

L. longiflorus Desr. in Lam., Encyc. Méth. Bot. 3: 598,
  (1789) = [1791].

188. *Varengevillea* Baill., Hist. des Pl. 11: 116, 1892.

V. hispidissima (Seem.) Baill., Hist. des Pl. 11: 116, 1892.

Colea hispidissima Seem., Linn. Soc. Lond., Trans. 23: 9,
  1860.

  See Perrier de la Bathie, Not. Syst. 13: 290-291, 1948.
  Moldenke, Phytologia 5: 149, 1955.

CHAPTER 3

200. *Aleurodiscus* Rab. ex Cke., Grevillea 3: 137, 1875.
Aleurodiscus Rab. ex Schroet. in Cohn, Crypt.-Fl. Schles.
1: 429, 1888.
Cyphella Fr., Syst. Mycol. 2: 201, 1822.
See Donk, Bot. Gard. Buitenzorg, Bul. III, 17: 156, 159–
160, 1941; 18: 88–89, 159, 1949; Reinwardtia 1:
206–208, 1951.
Rogers & Jackson, Farlowia 1: 269, 1944.
Rogers, Farlowia 3: 433, 1949; 4: 15, 1950.

201. *Erythrophyllum* Loeske, Hedwigia 47: 175, 1908.
Erythrophyllum Agardh, Lunds Univ. Ars-Skr., Afdeln. III
Math. & Naturvetsk. 8(6): 10–12, 1871.
Erythrobarbula Steere, Bryologist 54: 191, 1951.

202. *Penecillium frequetans* Series, Raper, Thom & Fennel, Man.
Penecillia 170, 1949.
P. frequetans Westling, Arkiv för Botanik 11: 133, fig. 39,
78, 1912.

203. *Spongodendron* Zanardini, Nuovo Giorn. Bot. Ital. 10: 37–
38, 1878.
Spongocladia Areschoug, Öfvers K. Vetensk.-Akad.,
Förhandl. 10: 201–209, 1853.
Cladophoropsis Boergesen, Overs, K. Danske Vidensk.
Selsk., Förhandl. 1905: 259–291, 1905.
See Papenfuss, Pacif. Sci. 4: 208–213, 1950.
Silva, Univ. Calif., Publ. Bot. 25: 271, 1952.
Taxon 3: 234, 1954; 4: 118, 1955.

204. *Peridinium depressum* Bailey, Smithsonian Inst., Contr.
Know. 7(3): 12–13, pl., fig. 33–38, 1855.
Ceratium divergens Claparède & Lachman, Inst. Natl.
Génév., Mem. 1859–1860, 7: 71, pl. 13, fig. 23, 1861,
non Ehrenberg (1840).

P. divergens Ehrenb. γ *reniforme* Ehrenb., Akad. Wissensch.
   Berlin, Ber. 240, 1854.

P. depressa Ostenfeld in Knudsen & Ostenf., Iagttagelser
   over Overfladevandets Temperatur, Wandel. 60, fig. 1,
   1900.

P. marinum Lindamann, Bot. Arch. 9: 98–99, fig. 7–12,
   1925.

   See Graham, Carnegie Inst. Wash., Publ. 542; 18–21,
      1942.

205. *Roscheria* H. Wendl. in Baker, Fl. Maurit. 386–387, 1877.
   Roscheria Wendl. in Papenfuss, Madroño 11: 29, 1951; repr.
      p. 4, 1951.
   Roschera Sonder in von der Decken, Reisen in Ost-Afrika
      in 1859–1865, 3(3): 81, pl. 1, fig. 5–11, 1879.
   Tolypiocladia Schmitz in Engler & Prantl, Natürl.
      Pflanzenfam. 1(2): 441–442, 1897; Engl. Bot. Jahrb. 21:
      160, 1895.

   See Silva, Univ. Calif., Publ. Bot. 25: 308, 1952.

206. *Tricholoma quercifolia* Murrill, Lloydia 12: 67, 1949.
   T. subfulvidiscum Murrill, Lloydia 12: 67, 1949.

207. *Halymenia Durvillaei* Bory var. *denudata* Weber-van Bosse,
   Siboga Exped., Monogr. 59b: 236, 1921.

208. *Lycopodium Hamiltonii* Spreng., in Syst. Veg. of Linnaeus,
   ed. 16 by Spreng. 5: 429, 1829; 4(1): 20, 1827; 4(1):
   12, 1827.

209. *Ahnfeltia concinna* J. Agardh, Ofvers K. Svensk. Vet. Akad.,
   Förhandl. 1847(1): 12, 1847.
   A. Gigartinoides J. Agardh, Ofvers. K. Svensk. Vet. Akad.,
      Förhandl. 1847(1): 12, 1847.
   A. concinna J. Agardh in Setchell & Gardner, Univ. Calif.
      Publ. Bot. 1: 305, 1903.
   A. Gigartinoides J. Agardh in G. M. Smith, Marine Algae
      Monterey Penin. Calif. 272, 1944.

210. *Peziza amorpha* Pers., Mycol. Eur. 1: 269, 1822.
   Thelephora amorpha (Pers.) Fries, Elenchus Fung. 1: 183,
      1828.
   Corticium amorphum (Pers.) Fries, Epicr. Syst. Mycol. 559,
      1838. See Saccardo, Syll. Fung. 6: 606, 1888.

Cyphella amorpha (Pers.) Quél., Ench. Fung. 215, 1886.

Aleurodiscus amorphus (Pers.) Rabenh., Fungi Eur. Exs.
    1,824, 1874; Hedwigia 13: 184, 1874.

A. grantii Lloyd, Mycol. Writ. 6: 927, fig. 1,668, 1920.

Nodularia balsamicola Peck, New York State Mus., Rept.
    24: 96, pl. 4, fig. 23–26, 1872.

    See Taxon 3: 234, 1954; 4: 118, 1955.

211. *Trichogloea Herveyi* Taylor, Hydrobiologia 3: 119–121,
    1951.

T. Herveyi Setchell in Howe in Britton, Fl. Bermuda 511,
    1918.

212. *Agardhiella* Schmitz, Flora 7: 441, 1889.

213. *Microsorium punctatum* (L.) Copel., Bishop Mus., Bul. 93:
    73, 1932.

Polypodium punctatum (L.) Sw., Schrad. Jour. 1800(2): 21,
    1801.

Acrostichum punctatum L., Sp. Pl., ed. 2, 2: 1,524, 1763.

214. *Marsilea* L., Gen. Pl., ed. 5, 485, 1754; Sp. Pl. 1,099, 1753.

215. *Goniolithon* Foslie, Kgl. Norske Vidensk. Selsk., Skrift. 2:
    5, 1898.

    See Setchell & Mason, Natl. Acad. Sci., Proc. 29: 87–97,
        1943.

216. *Albugo* Pers. ex S. F. Gray, Nat. Arr. Brit. Pl. 1: 540, 1821.

Cystopus Lév., Ann. Sci. Nat. Bot. III, 8: 371, 1847.

Cystopus De Bary, Ann. Sci. Nat. Bot. IV, 20: 31, 1863.

    See Ramsbottom, Jour. Bot. Brit. For. 54: 77, 1916; Brit.
        Mycol. Soc., Trans. 18: 315, 1934.

        Wakefield, Bothalia 2: 242–246, 1927.

        Fitzpatrick, The Lower Fungi: Phycomycetes 192,
            1930.

        Weatherby, Kew Bul. Misc. Inf. 421–422, 1935.

        Ainsworth & Bisby, Dict. Fungi 80, 1943; ed. 3, 91,
            1950.

        Rogers, Mycologia 40: 241–254, 1948; 42: 325–330,
            1950.

217. *Struthiopteris pensylvanica* Willd., Sp. Pl. of L., ed. 4 by
        Willd. 5: 289, 1810.

Onoclea Struthopteris (L.) Hoffm., Deutschl. Fl. 3: 11, 1795.

Matteucia Struthiopteris (L.) Todaro, Syn. Pl. Acot. Vasc.
        Sicilia 30, 1866.

Osmunda Struthiopteris L., Sp. Pl. 1,066, 1753.

Pteretis pensilvanica (Willd.) Fernald, Rhodora 47: 123,
      1945.

Matteucia Struthiopteris (L.) Todaro var. *pensylvanica*
      (Willd.) Morton, Am. Fern. Jour. 40: 247, 1950.

218. *Fumago* Pers., Mycol. Eur. 1: 9, 1822.
      See Berk. & Mont., Hort. Soc. Lond., Jour. 4: 244–245,
            1849.
            Woronich, Ann. Mycol. 24: 261–264, 1926.
            Bisby, Commonw. Mycol. Inst., Mimeogr. Publ. 6: 11,
                  1949.
            Rogers, Mycologia 40: 635–637, 1948; Farlowia 4:
                  17–18, 37–38, 1950.

219. *Lycopodium inundatum* L. var. *appressum* Chapm., Bot.
            Gaz. 3: 20, 1878.
      L. alopecuroides L. var. *adpressum* Chapm. emend., Fl. So.
            U. S., ed. 2, 671, 1883; ed. 3, 638, 1897.
      See Fernald, Rhodora 42: 405, 1940.

220. *Martensia* Hering, Ann. and Mag. Nat. Hist. 8: 92, 1842.
      Hemitrema R. Br. ex Endl., Mant. Bot. sistens Gen. Pl.,
            Suppl. 3: 50, 1843.
      Mesotrema J. Agardh, Övers K. Svenske Vetensk.-Akad.,
            Förhandl. 11: 110, 1854.
      Capraella De Toni f., Not. Nomencl. Alg. 7: 3, 1936.
      Martensia Giseke, Linn. Praelec. Ord. Nat. Pl., ed. Giseke
            199, 207, 249, 1792.
      Mertensia Roth, Catalect. Bot. 1: 34, 1797; HBK., Nov.
            Gen. Sp. 2: 30–32, pl. 103, 1817.
      See Papenfuss, Natl. Acad. Sci., Proc. 28: 448, 1942;
            Madroño 10: 182, 1950; Doty, Taxon 3: 229, 1954.
      Taxon 3: 234, 1954; 4: 118, 1955.

221. *Elizabethia miniata* Trevisan, Gazzetta Uffiziale di
            Venezia, anno 1855(53): 3, 1855, marzo 6.
            See de Toni, Archvio Botanico 14(3-4): 9–10, 1938.
            Silva, Univ. Calif., Publ. Bot. 25: 301, 1952.

222. *Aspidium scabriusculum* Davenp., Bot. Gaz. 21: 255–256,
            1896.
      Dryopteris scabriuscula Davenp., Bot. Gaz. 21: 256, 1896.

Nephrodium scabriusculum Davenp., Bot. Gaz. 21: 256, 1896.

Lastrea scabriuscula Davenp., Bot. Gaz. 21: 256, 1896.

223. *Cibotium NEALIAE* Degener in Degener & Hatheway, Fl. Haw. 5: fam. 12, 8/15/51.

C. glaucum var. *NEALIAE* Hatheway in Degener & Hatheway, Fl. Haw. 5: fam. 12, 8/15/51.

224. *Flammula* (Fr.) Kummer, Führer Pilzk. 22, 1871.

Flammula (DC.) Fourr., Soc. Linn. Lyon, Ann. II, 16: 324, 1868.

Gymnopilus Karst., Känned. Finl. Nat. Folk, Bidr. 32: xxi, 400, 1879.

See Dodoens, Stirp. Hist. Pempt. 399–400, 1553.

De Candolle, Reg. Veg. Syst. Nat. 1: 133, (1818) = [1817].

Wakefield, Brit. Mycol. Soc., Trans. 23: 227, 1939.

Donk, Bot. Gard. Buitenzorg, Bul. III, 17: 157, 166–168, 1941; 18: 95–96, 1949; 18: 328, 332, 1949.

Singer & Smith, Mycologia 38: 263, 291, 1946.

Rogers, Farlowia 3: 443, 1949; 4: 25, 1950.

225. *Lycopodium annotinum* L. forma *spica omacio sessile* Luerssen, Nordostdeutsche Waldfl., 1880.

L. annotinum L. lusus *proliferum* Aschers. & Graebn., Syn. Mitteleurop. Fl. 1: 152, 1896.

See Nessel, Die Bärlappgewächse 278, 1939.

226. *Uromyces appendiculatus* (Pers.) Link, Ges. Nat. Freunde Berlin, Mag. 7: 28, 1816.

Uredo appendiculata Pers., Ann. Bot. Usteri 15: 16–17, 1795; Syn. Meth. Fung. 221–222, 1801.

Uredo Pamparum Speg., Soc. Ci. Argent., Anal. 9: 173, 1880.

Uredo rufa (Bon.) Speg., Soc. Ci. Argent., Anal. 17: 124, 1884.

See Jackson, Mycologia 23: 351, 1931.

227. *Zanardinula Kylinii* Doty, Farlowia 3: 173, 1947.

Prionitis linearis Kylin, Univ. Lund., Arsk. N. F. 37(2): 12–13, pl. 4, fig. 11, 1941.

Z. linearis (Kylin) Papenfuss, Farlowia 1: 342, 1944.

P. linearis Kylin in Smith, Marine Algae Monterey Penin. 245, pl. 56, fig. 21, 1944.

Prionitis Agardh, Sp. Gen. Ord. Alg. 2: 185-191, 1851.

P. lanceolata Harvey sensu Collins, Holden & Setchell in
  Collins *et al.*, Phytotheca Bor. Am. fasc. 4: No. 199b,
  1896.

Gelidium ? *lanceolatum* Harvey in Hook. & Arn., Bot.
  Beechey Voy. 164, 409, 1841.

P. lanceolata (Harvey) Harvey, Smithsonian Inst., Contr. 5:
  197, pl. 27, fig. A, 1852.

Z. lanceolata (Harvey) de Toni, Noterelle di Nomencl. Alg.
  7: sixth page, unnumbered, 1936.

  See Taxon 3: 234, 1954; 4: 118, 1955.

228. *Andreaea* Ehrh., Hannov. Mag. 1778(or 16): 1,601-1,603,
  1779.

Andreaeaceae Lindb., Utkast 36, 1878.

Andreaeales Ruhland in Engler, Natürlichen Pflanzenfam.
  1(3): 262, 1909; ed. 2, 10: 126, 1924.

229. *Zonaria* Roussel, Flore du Calvados, ed. 2, 99-100, 1806.

Zonaria C. Agardh, Syn. Algarum Scand., p. XX, 1817.

Zonaria C. Agardh sensu Tandy, Brittonia 6: 37, 1947.

Zonaria C. Agardh sensu Papenfuss, Madroño 9: 9, 1947.

Gymnosorus J. Agardh, Analecta Algol., Contin. 1., Soc.
  Physiogr. Lund., Act. 29: 9-12, 1894.

Gymnosorus Trevisan, Saggia di monograf. alghe coccothalle
  108, 1848.

Orthosorus Trevisan, Linnaea 22: 457-461, 1849.

Pocockiella Papenfuss, Am. Jour. Bot. 30: 463-468, 1948.
  See Silva, Univ. Calif., Publ. Bot. 25: 272-277, 1952;
    Taxon 3: 234, 1954; 4: 118, 1955.

230. *Equisetum ramosissimum* Desf. Race III.—*E. campanulatum*
  Poir. β *scabrum* Hy, S.-var. *Renati* (Hy, l. c., pro var.)
  Nob., Rouy. Flore de France 14: 507, 1913.

E. ramosissimum Desf., Fl. Atlant. 2: 398-399, anno sexto
  (1800) =[1799]; see Stearn, Soc. Bibliog. Nat. Hist.,
  Jour. 1: 147-148, 1938.

E. campanulatum Poir. in Lam., Dict. 5: 613, 1804.

E. ramosissimum Desf. 1 *scabrum* Milde, Höheren Sporenpfl.
  Deutschl. & Schweiz 118, 1865.

231. *Urostachys erubescens* (Brack.) Herter ex Nessel, Die
  Bärlappgewächse 61, 1939.

Lycopodium erubescens Brack., U. S. Expl. Exped. Bot. 16:
320, pl. 45, fig. 1, 1854.

232. *Dumortiera hirsuta* (Sw.) Reinw. Bl. & Nees var. *nepalensis*
.(Tayl.) Frye & Clark, Hepat. N. Am. 93, 1937.
Hygropyla nepalensis Tayl., Linn. Soc. Lond., Trans. 17:
392, (1835) = [1837].
Dumortiera nepalensis (Tayl.) Nees, Naturg. Eur. Leberm.
4: 169, 1838.
D. hirsuta α *latior* Gottsche, Lind. & Nees, Syn. Hepat.
544, 1844.

233. *Dryopteris gongylodes* (Schk.) Ktze., Rev. Gen. Pl. 2: 811,
1891.
Aspidium goggilodus Schk., Vier und Zwanzig. Kl. Linn.
Krypt. Gewachse 1: 193; 2: pl. 33c, 1809.
Cyclosorus gongylodes (Schk.) Link, Hort. Reg. Bot. Berol.
2: 128, 1833.
Dryopteris goggilodus (Schk.) Fosb., Bishop Mus., Occ.
Pap. 16: 337–338, 1942.
See Skottsberg, Nat. Hist. Juan Fernandez & Easter I.,
2: 768, 1951.

234. *Polystichum aristatum* (Forst. f.) Presl var. *Voniifolium*
(Wall.) Farw., Am. Midl. Nat. 12: 261, 1931.
Aspidium aristatum (Forst. f.) Sw. β *A. Coniifolium* (Wall.)
Hook. & Baker, Syn. Fil. 255–256, 1874.
A. Coniifolium Wall., Cat. (Num. List Pl. E. Ind.) No. 341,
1828.
A. coniifolium Presl, Del. Prag. 1: 175, 1822.

235. *Ectocarpus Duchassaingianus* Grunow, ed. Fenzl, Reise der
Österreich. Fregatte Novara um die Erde, Bot. Theil. 1:
45, pl. 4, fig. 1, 1870.
See Silva, Univ. Calif., Publ. Bot. 25: 256, 1952.

236. *Nectria cytisporina* Ellis & Everh., Erythea 1: 197, 1893.

237. *Anthoceros* Micheli, Nova Genera Pl. 10, 1729.
Anthoceros [Micheli] L., Sp. Pl. 1,139, 1753.
Anthocerus L. ex Dillen., Hist. Musc. 11: 1768.
Ceranthus L., Fund. Bot. of Linnaeus, ed. Gilibert, 3: 466,
1787 (Gilibert, Syst. Pl. Eur. 7: 466, 1787).
Corypta Necker, Elem. Bot. 344, 1790.
Carpoceros Du Mortier, Comment. Bot. 76, 1822.

Carpoceras DC., Mus. Paris, Mém. 7: 234, 1821.

Anthoceras L. ex Brongn. & Dec., Ann. Sci. Nat. Bot. V, 20: 325, 1874.

Aspiromitus Steph., Sp. Hepat. 5: 957, 1916.

See Proskauer, Ann. Bot. n.s., 12: 262, 1948.

238. *Pauahia sideroxyli* Stevens, Bishop Mus., Bul. 19: 17-18, fig. 2, 1925.

239. *Langermannia* Rostk. in Sturm, Deutschl. Fl. 3(5): 3, 23, 1844.

Calvatia Fr., Summa Veg. Scand. 2: 442, 1849.

See Perdeck, Blumea 6: 486, 1950.

240. *Raciborskiomyces* Siemaszko, Soc. Bot. Pol., Act. 2: 270, 1925.

Chatyllis Clements in Clements & Shear, Gen. Fungi 253, 1931.

241. *Sphaeria picea* Pers., Icon. Descr. Fung. 2: 40, pl. 10, fig. 7-8, 1800.

S. picea Pers. ex Fr., Syst. Mycol. 2(2): 431, 1823.

Diaporthe Euporthe picea (Pers.) Sacc., Syll. Fung. 1: 648, 1882.

242. *Mycosphaerella elymifoliae* Munk, Dansk Bot. Ark. 14(8): 2, 1952.

243. *Cladophora Aegagropila Sibogae* Rbld. ex Weber, Siboga Exped., Monogr. 59a: 81-82, fig. 19, 1913.

C. (Aegagr.) Sibogae Rbld., Nuova Notarisia 16: 146, 1905.

See Taxon 3: 234, 1954; 4: 118, 1955.

244. *Euzodiomyces* Thaxt., Am. Acad. Arts Sci., Proc. 35: 449, 1900.

245. *Peniophora ludoviciana* Burt, Mo. Bot. Gard., Ann. 12: 244, 1925.

246. *Puccinia* Pers., Syn. Meth. Fung. xv, index, 1801.

Pvccinia Pers., Syn. Meth. Fung. 225-230, 1801.

247. *Pellicularia* Cke., Grevillea 4: 116, 1876.

248. *Fimbriaria Bolanderi* Austin, Acad. Nat. Sci. Phila., Proc. 1869: 230, (1869) = [1870].

Asterella Bolanderi (Austin) Underw., Bot. Gaz. 20: 61, 1895.

See Silva, Univ. Calif., Publ. Bot. 25: 269, 1952.

249. *Leptodontium humillimum* Broth., Rijks Herb. Leiden,
Meded. 14: 17, fig. 1, 1912.

250. *Epichloe* (Fr.) Tul., Sel. Fung. Carpol. 3: 24, 1865.
Epichloe Fr., Summa Veg. Scand. 381, 1849.
Epichloë (Fr.) Tul. ex Atkins., Torr. Bot. Club, Bul. 21:
224, 1894.

251. *Cladonia subrangiformis* Sandst., Naturw. Ver. Bremen,
Abhandl. 25: 165, 1922.
C. subrangiformis Scriba ex Sandst., in Rabenh., Krypt. Fl.
Deutschl. Oesterr. Schw. 9(4²): 231, 1931.
C. furcata (Huds.) Schrad. *C. subrangiformis* (Sandst.) Des
Abbayes, Soc. Sci. Bretagne, Bul. 14: 154, 1937.
See Evans, Rhodora 56: 267, 1954.

252. *Agaricus Persoonii* Fr., Syst. Mycol. 1: 27, 1821.
A. Persooniana Phillips & Plowr., Grevillea 10: 66, 1881.

253. *Boudiera* Cke., Grevillea 6: 76, 1877.

254. Brongiart, Essai Class Champ. 1825.

255. *Gaultheria* Kalm in L., Gen. Pl., ed. 5, 187, 1754.
Gautiera Raf., Med. Fl. 1: 202, 1828.
Gautieria Vitt., Mon. Tuber. 25, 1831.
Gualteria Raf., Fl. Tellur. 1: 18, (1836) = [1837].
Gaultiera Raf., Fl. Tellur. 1: 18, (1836) = [1837].
See Rogers, Farlowia 4: 25–26, 1950.

256. *Boletus Tulipiferae* Schw., Naturf. Ges. Leipzig, Schr. 1:
99, 1822.
Irpex tulipifera (Schw.) Schw. ex Fries, Epicr. Syst. Myc.
523, 1838; Overh., Mo. Bot. Gard., Ann. 1: 152, 1914.
Polyporus tulipiferus Schw. ex Overh., Wash. Univ., Stud.
3(1), No. 1: 29, pl. 3, fig. 11a-c, 1915.

257. *Ravenelia* Berk., Gard. Chron. No. 9: 132, fig. 1–2, 1853,
Feb. 26.

258. *Höhnelogaster* Lohwag, Bot. Centralbl., Beih. 42(2): 299,
1926.
Hoehneliogaster Lohwag emend. E. Fisch., in Engler &
Prantl, Natürl. Pflanzenfam., ed. 2, 7a: 23, 1933.

259. *Helotium* ? *brassicaecolum* (Schw.) Sacc., Syll. Fung. 8:
226, 1889.

Sarea brassicaecola Schw., Am. Phil. Soc., Trans. II, 4:
    178, 1832.

260. *Agaricales* Clements ex Singer, sensu strictiore, Lilloa 22:
    126, (1949l = [1951].
    Agaricales Clements, Gen. Fungi 102, 1909; Rea, Brit. Bas.
        xi, 1922.

261. *Lenormandia coronata* Lindauer & Setch. in Lindauer, Algae
    Nova-Zelandicae Exsiccatae 74: 1940; Lindauer &
    Setch., R. S. New Zealand, Trans. 76(1): 66–68, pl. 1,
    1946.
        See Taxon 3: 234, 1954; 4: 118, 1955.

262. *Enteromorpha compressa constricta* J. Agardh in M. A.
    Howe, Torrey Bot. Club, Bul. 57: 605, 1931.
    E. compressa (L.) Grev. b. *constricta* J. Agardh, Lunds
        Univ., Arsskrift 19: 138, 1882–1883.
        See Taxon 3: 234, 1954; 4: 118, 1955.

263. *Chlorococcum* E. M. Fries, Syst. Mycol. 1: XXII, 1821; 2:
    272, 1825.
    Tremella botryoides (L.) Schreber, Spicil. Fl. Lips. 141,
        1771.
    Byssus botryoides L., Sp. Pl. 1,169, 1753.
    Nostoc Botryoides (L.) Agardh, Syn. Alg. Scand. 135, 1817.
    Protococcus botryoides (Kuetz.) Kirchn., in Cohn, Kryptog.
        Fl. Schlesien 2(1): 103, 1878.
        See Silva, P. C. & Starr, R. C., Svensk Bot. Tidskr. 47:
            234–247, 1953.

264. *Hymenophyllum polyanthum* Hook. in Nightingale, Thos.,
    Oceanic Sketches 132, 1835.
    Trichomanes polyanthos (Hook.) Hook., Sp. Fil. 1: 138,
        1846; Hooker's Icones 8: text and pl. 703, 1848.
        See Copel., Philipp. Jour. Sci. 51: 230, 1933;
            Ballard, Pacif. Sci. 10: 269–270, 1956.

265. *Alsophila ? polypodioides* Hook. in Thomas Nightingale,
    Oceanic Sketches 131, 1835.
    Dryopteris ornata (Wall.) C. Chr., Ind. Fil. 281, 1905.
    Polypodium ornatum Wall., Cat. (Num. List Pl. E. Ind.), No.
        327, 1829.

P. ornatum Wall. ex Beddome, Ferns S. India 56, pl. 171, 1863-1865.

See C. Chr., Bishop Mus., Bul. 177: 94, 1943.

266. F. Hildeb. = Hildebrand, Friedrich Hermann Gustav (1835-1915). Determine abbreviations for: Hildebrandt, Johann Maria (1847-1881); Hillebrand, William (1821-1886); Hillebrandt, Franz (1805-1860); Hill, John (1716-1775); Hill, Albert Frederick (1889-   ); Hill, Sir Arthur William (1875-1941).

267. *Polygonum convolvuloides* Bruger forma *intermedium* Lawalrée, Bruxelles Jard. Bot. État, Bul. 22(3-4): 211-212, fig. 26A, 1952.

P. convolvuloides Bruger forma *pterocarpum* Lawalrée, Bruxelles Jard. Bot. Etat, Bul. 22(3-4): 212-213, fig. 26B, 1952.

268. *Pseudendoclonium arctica* Prescott, Am. Midl. Nat. 50: 467-468, (1953) = [1954].

269. *Fucus scoparius* Strøm, Physisk og Oeconomisk Beskr. Fogderiet Søndmør Bergens Norge 1: 93-94, 1762; Beskrivelse Norske Søe-Vaexter 250-252, pl. f, fig. 1, 1770.

Laminaria scoparia (Strøm) Du Rietz, Bot. Notis 1920: 42, 1920.

Fucus hyperboreus Gunnerus, Fl. Norveg. 1: 34-35, pl. 3, 1766.

Laminaria hyperborea (Gunn.) Foslie, Christiania Vidensk.-Selsk., Forhandl. 14: 41-54, 1884; repr. as Ueber Laminar. Norveg. 41-54, 1884.

Fucus digitatus L., Mantissa 134, (1771) = [1767].

Fucus digitatus Huds., Fl. Angl. 474, 1762.

Laminaria digitata (Huds.) Lamx., Nat. Hist. Mus. Paris, Ann. 20: 42, 1813; repr. as Essai Gen. Thalassiophytes non Articulées 42, 1813.

Fucus scoparius Huds., Fl. Angl. 471, 1762.

See Du Rietz, Svensk Bot. Tidskr. 47: 16-23, 1953; Silva, Univ. Calif., Publ. Bot. 25: 260, 1952.

270. *Scyphofilix trrigosa* (Thunb.) Farw. var. *hirta* (Kaulf.) Farw., Am. Midl. Nat. 12: 263, 1931.

Trichomanes strigosum Thunb., Fl. Jap. 339–340, 1784.
Davallia hirta Kaulf., Enum. Fil. 223, 1824.
Scyphofilix Thouars, Gen. Nov. Madag. 1, 1806; Roemer,
    Collect. Bot. 195, 1809.

271. *Lecanora raroia* Herre, Bryologist 56: 279–280, 1953.

272. *Verrubotrytis* Buchwald, Roy. Vet. & Agric. Coll. Copen-
    hagen, Dept. Pl. Path., Contr. 32: 146, 148, 1949.

273. *Sphaerobotryotinia* Buchwald, Roy. Vet. & Agric. Coll.
    Copenhagen, Dept. Pl. Path., Contr. 32: 137, 1949.

274. *Streptomyces albo-niger* Hesseltine, J. N. Porter, Deduck,
    Hauck, Bohonos & J. H. Williams, Mycologia 46: 19,
    1954.

275. *Verticilliodochium tubercularioides* (Speg.) Bubàk, Ann.
    Mycol. 12: 220, pl. 8, 1914.
    Verticillis tuberculis (Speg.) Bubàk ex Clements & Shear,
        Gen. Fungi 220, 401, 1931.
    Verticillium tubercularioides Speg., Fungi Argentini
        Pugillus 4: No. 329, 1882; Soc. Ci. Argent. 13: 25,
        1882.

276. *Aecidium* Pers. in Gmel., Syst. Nat. of Linnaeus, ed. 13 by
    Gmel., 2(2): 1,472, 1791.
    Oecidium Lév., in D'Orbigny, Dict. 1: 137, 1861.
    See Arthur, J. C., Man. Rusts U. S. & Can. 380, 1934.

277. *Geminispora* Pat., Soc. Mycol., Bul. 9: 151, 1893.
    Diplosporis Clements, Gen. Fungi 27, 1909.

278. *Zygnema insigne* (Hass.) Kütz. var. *confusospora* Habeeb,
    Rhodora 56: 42, 1954.
    See Silva, Univ. Calif., Publ. Bot. 25: 253, 1952.

279. *Bulgaria* Fries, Syst. Myc. 2(1): 166, (1823) = [1822].
    B. globosa Fries, Syst. Myc. 2(1): 166–167, (1823) = [1822].
    B. inquinans (Pers.) Fries, Syst. Myc. 2(1): 167, (1823) =
        [1822].
    Phaeobulgaria inquinans (Fr.) Seav., Mycologia 24: 253,
        1932.
    P. inquinans (Fr.) Nannf., Reg. Soc. Sci. Upsala, Nova
        Acta, IV, 8(2): 311, 1932.

Bulgaria Fries ex Kobayashi, Jour. Jap. Bot. 13: 510–520,
    1937.
  See Seaver, N. Am. Cup Fungi (Inoperculates), 1951.

280. *Sagenia plataphylla* J. Sm., Hooker's Jour. Bot. 3: 410,
    1841.
  S. platyphylla J. Sm. emend., Ferns Brit. & For., rev. ed.,
    145, 1879.
  Aspidium platyphyllum (Willd.) Mett., Fil. Hort. Bot. Lips.
    88, pl. 22, fig. 1–2, 1856.
  A. platyphyllum Willd., Sp. Pl. of Linnaeus, ed. 4 by Willd.
    5: 255, 1810.
  A. platyphyllum (J. Sm.) Presl, Epim. 65, 1849.

281. *Diplodina persicae* Horn & Hawthorne, Phytopath. 44: 134–
    136, fig. 1, 1954.

282. *Cordyceps* Fr., Obs. Mycol. 2: 316, 1818.
  Cordyceps Link, Handb. Gew. 3: 346, 1833.
  Cordylia Fr., Obs. Mycol. 2: 316, 1818.
  Cordylia Fr. ex Ficinus & Schubert, Fl. Dresden, ed. 2, 2:
    331, 1823.
  Cordylia Pers., Syn. Pl. 2: 260, 1807.
  Cordyceps Fr., Summ. Veg. Scand. 381, 1849.
  Sphaeria ser. I *Cordyliae* Fr., Myk. 2: [33], 1823.
  Sphaeria sect. I *Periphericae* trib. *Cordyceps* Fr., Syst.
    Mycol. 2(2): 320, 323, 1823.
  See Farlowia 3: 438, 1949;
    Mycologia 46: 248–249, 1954.

283. *Acharospora alboatra* H. Magn., Bot. Staatssaml. München,
    Mitt. 9–10: 451, 1954.

284. *Noteroclada* Tayl. ex Hook & W. Wilson, Hooker's London
    Jour. Bot. 3: 166, 1844.
  Noteroclada Tayl. in Hook. f. & Thos. Taylor, Hooker's
    London Jour. Bot. 3: 477–478, 1844.
  Androcryphia Nees in Gottsche, Lindenberg & Nees, Syn.
    Hepatic. 470–471, 1844.
  See Taxon 3: 233, 1954.
    Proskauer, Bryologist 58: 192–198, 1955.

285. *Herbertus* S. F. Gray, Nat. Arr. Brit. Pl. 684–685, 1821.
  Herverus S. F. Gray, Nat. Arr. Brit. Pl. 685, 1821.

Herberta S. F. Gray emend. Lindb., Soc. Sci. Fenn., Acta
  10: 516, 1875.
Pallavicinius S. F. Gray, Nat. Arr. Brit. Pl. 775, 1821.
Papa S. F. Gray, Nat. Arr. Brit. Pl. 686, 1821.
  See Le Jolis, Cherbourg, Soc. Nat. Sci. Nat. Math., Mém.
    29: 16, 1893.
    Evans, Bryologist 40: 25–33, 1937.

286. *Rhytisma astericolum* Sacc., Syll. Fung. 8: 762, 1889.

287. *Lithophyllum* Hariot, sp. nov., Ministères Marine & Inst.
  Publ., Miss. Sci. Cap Horn, Bot. 5: 84, 1889.

288. *Chrysophaeum* Lewis & Bryan, Am. Jour. Bot. 28: 343–348,
  63 figs., 1941.
  Chrysophaeum Taylor, Hydrobiologia 3: 122–130, 1951.
  Chrysonephos Taylor, Torrey Bot. Club, Bul. 79: 79, 1952.

289. *Rhizophidium difficile* Canter, Brit. Mycol. Soc., Trans. 37:
  119–121, fig. 4, 1954.

290. *Albocrustum* McG. ex Lloyd, Mycol. Writ. 7: 1,353–1,354, pl.
  333, fig. 3,167–3,168, 1925.
  Albocrustum LLoyd (as McGinty) teste Stevenson & Cash,
    Lloyd Libr. & Mus., Bul. 35 (Mycol., Ser. 8): 4, 1936.

291. *Polyporus Fijii* Lloyd, Mycol. Writ. 7: 1,112, pl. 194, fig.
  2,077, 1922.

292. *Globosopyreno* Lloyd, Mycol. Writ. 7: 1,178, pl. 231, fig.
  2,361–2,362, 1923.

293. *Filicula bulbifera* (L.) Farw., Am. Midl. Nat. 12: 251, 1931.
  Polypodium bulbiferum L., Sp. Pl. 1,091, 1753.
  Cystopteris bulbifera (L.) Bernh., Schrad, Neu Jour. 1(2):
    10, 1806.

294. *Fomes arctostaphyli* Long, New Mexico Chapter Phi Kappa
  Phi, Papers 1: 2–3, 1917; Overholts, Polyporaceae
  U. S., Alaska, Can. 60, 1953.
  Boletus igniarius L., Sp. Pl. 1,176, 1753.
  Polyporus igniarius L. ex Fries, Syst. Myc. 1: 375, 1821.
  Fomes igniarius (L. ex Fries) Kickx., Fl. Crypt. Flandres
    2: 237, 1867.

295. *Itajahya* Möll., Bras. Pilzblumen 79, 148, 1895.

296. *Trachyspora* Fuckel, Bot. Zeit. 19: 250, 1861.
Trechispora Karst., Hedwigia 29: 147, 1890.
See Rogers, Mycologia 36: 75, 1944.

297. *Hypnum torquatum* Sw., Prodr. Ind. Occ. 142, 1788.
H. torquatum Hedw., Sp. Musc. 246, 1801.
Schlotheimia torquata (Sw. ex Hedw.) Brid., Bryol. Univ. 1:
323, 1826.

298. *Gertrudia* Herzog, Bibl. Bot. 87: 44, 1916.

299. *Ceriosporopsis halima* Linder in Barghoorn & Linder,
Farlowia 1: 408–409, pl. 3, fig. 10–12, 1944.
Helicoma salinum Linder in Barghoorn & Linder, Farlowia
1: 406–407, 1944.

CHAPTER 4

300. *Thelypteris spinulosa* (O. F. Muell.) Nieuwl., var. *dilatata*
(Hoffm.) St. John, Bot. Dept., State Coll. Wash., Contr.
2: 1, 1925.

Polypodium dilatatum Hoffm., Deutschl. Fl. 3: 7-8, 1795;
Fl. Germ. 2: 7-8, 1795.

Aspidium spinulosum (O. F. Muell.) Willd. var. *dilatatum*
(Hoffm.) Hook., Brit. Fl. 444, 1830.

Dryopteris spinulosa (O. F. Muell.) Ktze. var. *dilatata*
(Hoffm.) Underw., Nat. Ferns & Allies, ed. 4, 116-117,
1893.

Nephrodium dilatatum (Hoffm.) Desv., Soc. Linn. Paris,
Mém. 6: 261, 1827; repr. as Prodr. 261, 1827.

301. *Sabal louisiana* (Darby) Bomhard, Wash. Acad. Sci., Jour.
25: 44, 1935.

Chamaerops louisiana Darby, Geogr. Descript. Louisiana
194, 205-206, 216, 1816.

Sabal Deeringiana Small, Torreya 26: 34, 1926.

S. ? adiantinum Raf., Fl. Ludov. 17, 1817.

302. *Juglans pecan* Marshall, Arbustr. Am. 69, 1785.

Hicoria Pecan (Marsh.) Britt., Torrey Bot. Club, Bul. 15:
282, 1888.

Hicorius Pecan (Marsh.) Sarg., Gard. & For. 2: 460, 1889.

Iuglans illinoinensis Wang., Nordam. Holz. 54-55, pl. 18 or
fig. 43, 1787.

Carya illinoënsis (Wang.) K. Koch, Dendr. 1: 593-594,
1869.

Scoria Raf., Med. Repos. 11(ser. 2, 5:): 352, 1808.

Hickorius Raf., Fl. Ludov. 109, 1817.

Carya Nutt., Gen. Am. Pl. 2: 220-222, 1818.

See Sargent, Bot. Gaz. 66: 229-258, 1918.

Rehder, Jour. Arn. Arb. 22: 571, 1941.

Little, Am. Midl. Nat. 29: 493-508, 1943.

Fernald, Rhodora 49: 194-196, 1947.

Lawrence, Gent. Herb. 8(1): 25, 1949.

303. *Hernandria* Plum. ex L., Gen. Pl., ed. 5, 421, 1754.
   Hernandia Plum. ex L., Sp. Pl. 981, index, 1753.

304. *Acer rubrum* L., Sp. Pl. 1,055, 1753.
   A. carolinianum Walt., Fl. Carol. 251, 1788.
   Rufacer rubrum (L.) Small, Man. S. E. Fl. 826, 1,505, 1933.
   R. carolinianum (Walt.) Small, Man. S. E. Fl. 826, 1,505,
      1933.
   A. stenocarpum Britt. in Britt. & Shafer, N. Am. Trees 647,
      fig. 598, 1908.
   A. stenocarpum Ettinghausen, K. Bayer. Akad. Wiss.
      München, Denkschr. 50: 20, pl. 31, fig. 10–12, 1885.

305. *Iresine celosia* L. grex *lutescens* Suesseng., Bot.
   Staatssammlung München, Mitt. 4: 106, 1952.

306. *Terminalia mollis* Teysmann & Binnendijk, Cat. Bot. Gard.
      Buitenzorg 252, 1855; 237, 1866.
   T. mollis M. Laws. in Oliver, Fl. Trop. Afr. 2: 417, 1899.
   T. mollis (Presl) Rolfe, Jour. Bot. Brit. For. 23: 212, 1885.
   Pentaptera mollis Presl, Epim. Bot. 214, 1852; Kgl. Böhm.
      Gesell. Wiss., Abh., V, 6: 574, 1851.
      See van Steenis, Jard. Bot. Buitenzorg, Bul. III, 13: 117–
         119, 1933.

307. *Aconitum Napellus* L. β *alpinum* Regel, Lusus α *ambiguum*
      (Turcz.) Regel, Ann. Sci. Nat. Bot. IV, 16: 150, 1862.
   A. ambiguum Turcz., Fl. Baic. Dah. 1: 81, 1842.

308. *Rafinesquia* Raf., Sylva Tellur. 79, 1838.
   Rafinesquia Raf., Fl. Tellur. 1: 17, (1836) =[1837]; 2(1):
      96, (1836) =[1837].
   Rafinesquia Raf., Fl. Tellur. 3: 82, (1836) =[1837].
   Rafinesquia Nutt., Am. Phil. Soc., Trans. II, 7: 429, 1841.

309. *Hydrocotyle cordata* Walt., Fl. Carol. 113, 1788.
   Anonymos aquatica Walt., Fl. Carol. 108–109, 1788.
   Nymphodes aquaticum (Walt.) Ktze., Rev. Gen. Pl. 2: 429,
      1891; 3: 202, 1893.
   Nymphoides [Tourn.] Medic., Phil. Bot. 1: 35, 1789.
      See Fernald, Rhodora 42: 297–298, 1940.

310. *Pinus palustris* Mill., Gard. Dict., ed. 8, Pinus No. 14,
      1768.

P. palustris Willd., Sp. Pl. of Linnaeus, ed. 4 by Willd.,
   4(1): 499, 1805.
P. australis Michx. f., Hist. Arbr. For. Amér. Sept. 1: 64-
   85, pl. 6, 1810.
   See Fernald, Rhodora 50: 181-186, 241-249, 1948.
      Little, Phytologia 2: 457-458, 1948.

311. *Atacciae cristatae* (Jack) Haudricourt, Rev. Bot. Appliq. 22:
   73, 1941.
A. schizocapsae Haudr., Rev. Bot. Appliq. 22: 74, 1941.

312. *Gardenia Remyi* Mann, Am. Acad. Arts Sci., Proc. 7: 171,
   1867.
G. Remyi St. John, Brittonia 6: 438-444, fig. 4, a-f, 5, 7,
   1949.

313. *Microstylis* (Nutt.) Lindl., Orchid. Scel. 17, 1826.
Microstylis (Nutt.) Eaton, Man. Bot. N. Am., ed. 3, 353,
   1822.
Malaxis Soland. ex Sw., Nov. Gen. et Sp. Pl. seu Prodr.
   119, 1788.
   See Taxon 3: 240, 1954.

314. *Oenothera Hookeri* T. & G. ssp. *eu-Hookeri* Munz, El Aliso
   2(1): 11, 1949.
O. Hookeri T. & G. var. *eu-Hookeri* Munz, El Aliso 2(1): 11,
   adnot., 1949.

315. *Broussaisia arguta* Gaud. var. *arguta* Fosb. forma *arguta*
   Fosb., Bishop Mus., Occas. Pap. 15: 56, 1939.

316. *Claytonia depressa* (Gray) Suksd. var. *latifolia* Suksd.,
   Deutsch. Bot. Monatschr. 16: 222, 1898.
Montia latifolia Suksd., Deutsch. Bot. Monatschr. 16: 222,
   1898.

317. *Rudbeckia purpurea.* *serotina ǂ Nutt., Fraser's Cat. 1813;
   repr. in Pittonia 2: 118, 1890.
R. serotina Nutt., Acad. Nat. Sci. Phila., Jour. 7: 80-81,
   1834.
   See Shinners, Rhodora 57: 290-293, 1955;
      Graustein, Rhodora 58: 20-22, 1956;
      Cronquist *et al.,* Rhodora 58: 23-24, 1956;
      Shinners, Rhodora 58: 281-289, 1956;
      Cronquist, Rhodora 59: 100, 1957.

318. *Thryocephalon nemorale* J. R. & G. Forst., Char. Gen. 129,
   pl. 65, 1776.
   Kyllinga nemoralis (J. R. &. G. Forst.) Dandy in Hutchinson
      & Dalziel, Fl. W. Trop. Afr. 2: 486–487, 1936.
   K. monocephala Rottb., Descr. et Icon. Nov. Pl. 13, pl. 4,
      fig. 4, 1773, partim.
   Cyperus Kyllingia Endl., Cat. Hort. Acad. Vindob. 1: 94,
      1842.
   Scirpus Cephalotes L., Sp. Pl., ed. 2, 1: 76, 1762.
   Schoenus Cephalotes (L.) Rottb., Descr. et Icon. Nov. Pl.
      61, pl. 20, 1773.

319. *Victoria Regia* Lindl., Victoria Regia 3, col. pl., 1837.
   Nymphaea Victoria Schomburgk ex Lindl., Monogr. 3, 1837.
   Euryale amazonica Poeppig, Notizen aus den Gebiete der
      Natur- und Heilkunde, ed. Froriep 35: 131–132, 1832.
   Victoria regina Schomb. ex J. E. Gray, Mag. Zool. & Bot.
      2: 440, 1838.
   V. regalis Schomb., Mag. Zool. & Bot. 2: pl. 12, 1838.
   Anneslea amazonica Presl, Bot. Bemerk. 103, 1844.
   V. amazonum Klotzsch, Bot. Zeit. 5: 245, 1847.
   V. reginae Hook., Kew Jour. 2: 314, 1850.
   V. Cruziana D'Orbigny, Ann. Sci. Nat. Bot. II, 13: 57, 1840.
   V. amazonica (Poepp.) Sowerby, Ann. & Mag. Nat. Hist. II,
      6: 310, 1850.

320. *Charpentiera* Gaud. in Freyc., Voy. Bot. Uranie 444, pl. 47,
      48, (1826) =[1829].
   Carpenteria Torr., Smithsonian Contr. 6: 12–13, pl. 7, 1854.
   Carpentaria Becc., Jard. Bot. Buitenz., Ann. 2: 128, 1885.
   Carpentiera Steud., Nomencl. Bot., ed. 2, 1: 344, 1840.

321. *Abies* Hill, Brit. Herb. 509–510, 1756.
   Abies Bertol., Amoen. Ital. 287, pl. 4, fig. 2,a,c, 1819.

322. *Acoelorraphe* Wendl., Bot. Zeit. 37: 148, 1879.
   Acoeloraphe Wendl. ex Becc., Webbia 2: 107, 1907.
   Acanthosabal Proschowsky, Gard. Chron. III, 77: 91–92,
      fig. 35–38, 1925.
   Paurotis O. F. Cook, Torrey Bot. Club, Mem. 12: 21–23,
      1902.
      See Moore, Gent. Herb. 8: 209–215, 1951.

323. *Trematolobelia macrostachys* (H. & A.) Zahlbr. in Rock var.
grandifolia Rock, Coll. Hawaii Publ., Bul. 2: 46, 1913.
T. grandifolia Degener, Fl. Haw. fam. 339: 4/20/'34.

324. *Macaranga Maudslayi* Horne, A Year in Fiji 264, 1881; Baker
in Linn. Soc. Lond., Bot., Jour. 20: 371, 1883; Pax &
Hoffm., Engler's Pflanzenreich IV, 147(7): 394, 1914.
See A. C. Smith, Jour. Arn. Arb. 33: 390, 1952.

325. *Albizzia calliandra* Egler, Key to the Common Leguminosae
of the Hawaiian Is., First Manuscript Ed. 34, 1940.

326. *Torreya* Arn., Ann. Nat. Hist. 1: 126–132, 1838.
T. californica Torr., New York Jour. Pharm. 3: 49–51, 1854.
T. Myristica Hook., Curtis's Bot. Mag. 80: pl. 4,780, 1854.
Tumion Raf., Good Book and Amenities of Nature 62–63,
1840.
Tumion californicum (Torr.) Greene, Pittonia 2: 195, 1891.
Caryotaxus Zucc. ex Henkel & Hochst., Synops. Nadelh.
365, 1865.
Foetaxus J. Nelson (as Senilis), Pinaceae 167, 1866.
Torreya Spreng., Neue Entdeck. 2: 121–122, 1821.
Torreya Eaton, Man. Bot. N. Am., ed. 5, 420, 1829.

327. *Brachycome* Superspecies *tenuiscapa* G. L. Davis, Linn.
Soc. N. S. W., Proc. 73(3): 152, 1948.

328. *Andruris palawensis* Tuyama, Bot. Mag. Tokyo 52: 63, 1938.
A. elegans Giesen, in Engler's Pflanzenreich 18: 25, fig.
5, 1–4, 1938.
See Hosokawa, Jour. Jap. Bot. 16: 540, 1940.

329. *Hosta japonica* (Thunb.) Voss, Vilmorin's Blumengaertn. 1:
1,070, 1896.
Aletris japonica Thunb., Reg. Soc. Sci. Upsal., Nov. Acta
3: 208, 1780.
Hemerocallis Japonica Thunb., Fl. Japon. 142–143, 1784.
Hemerocallis lancifolia Thunb., Linn. Soc. Lond., Trans. 2:
335, 1794.
Hosta lancifolia (Thunb.) Tratt., Archiv Gewächsk. 1: 55,
1812.
See Stearn, Gard. Chron. III, 89: July 11, 27; July 18,
48–49; Aug. 1, 88–89; Aug. 8, 110, 1931.
Bailey, Gent. Herb. 2: 129–131, 1930; 2: 435, 1932.

330. *Rhynchospora lavarum* Gaud., Voy. Freyc. Coquille 415, 1826.

    R. glauca Vahl var. *chinensis* (Boeck.) C. B. Clarke forma *lavarum* (Gaud.) Kük. ex Skottsb., Göteborg Trädg., Meddel. 2: 213, 1925.

    R. glauca Vahl ssp. *lavarum* (Gaud.) Kük., Engler's Bot. Jahrb. 75: 150, 1950.

    Schoenus rugosus Vahl, Eclog. Am. 2: 5, 1798.

    R. rugosa (Vahl) Gale, Rhodora 46: 275–278, pl. 835, fig. 1A, 1944.

331. *Biotia* D. Don in Lamb., Pinet., ed. 2, 2: 129, 1828.

    Biotia DC., Prodr. 5: 264, 1836.

    Biotia Cass., Dict. Sci. Nat. 34: 308, 1825.

    Biotia Lamb., Descr. Gen. Pinus 2: 129, 1832.

332. *Frullania helleri* Stephani, Herb. Boissier, Bul. 5: 845–846, 1897.

    F. helleri Steph. in Rechinger, Bot.-Zool. Ergebn. Samoa, Neuguinea, Salomoninseln 3: 19, 1910.

333. *Saurauia roseotincta* R. E. Schultes, Harvard Univ., Bot. Mus. Leafl. 16(4): 83–86, 1953.

    See Rickett, Taxon 4: 185–188, 1955.

334. *Selaginurus* Herter, and *Selagina* Herter, Die Bärlapp-gewächse, 21, 22, 27, 1939.

335. *Picea Sitchensis* (Bong.) Carr., Traité Gén. Conif. 260–261, 1855.

    Pinus sitchensis Bong., Acad. Imp. Sci. St. Petersbourg, sér. 6, Sci. Math. Phys. Nat., Mem. 2: 164, 1832 (August).

    Pinus Menziesii Dougl. ex D. Don in Lamb., Descr. Genus Pinus, ed. 3, (octavo), 2: unnumbered page between pp. 144 and 145, 1832.

336. *Gifola* Cass., Soc. Philom., Paris, Bul. Sci. 142, 1819.

    Filago P. Loefling in L., Gen. Pl., ed. 5, 397, 1754; Sp. Pl. 927, 1753.

    Ifloga Cass., Soc. Philom., Paris, Bul. Sci. 142, 1819.

    Oglifa Cass., Soc. Philom., Paris, Bul. Sci. 143, 1819.

    Lofgia de Toni, Archivio Botanico 14(3–4): 19, 1938.

    Logfia Cass., Soc. Philom., Paris, Bul. Sci. 143, 1819.

337. *Rivinia humilis* L., Sp. Pl. 1: 121–122, 1753.

R. humilis L. α *canescens* L., Sp. Pl. 122, 1753.

338. *Putranjiva formosana* Kanehira & Sasaki, in Shimada, Nat.
Hist. Soc. Formosa, Trans. 24: 83, 1934.

Drypetes formosana (Kanehira & Sasaki) Kanehira, Formosan
Trees, rev. ed., 336, fig. 292, 1936.

339. *Amorpha nana* Nutt., Fraser's Cat. 1813; repr. in Pittonia 2:
116, 1890.

A. microphylla Pursh, Fl. Am. Sept. 466–467, 1814.
See Shinners, Rhodora 57: 290–293, 1955;
Cronquist *et al.,* Rhodora 58: 23–24, 1956;
Shinners, Rhodora 58: 281–289, 1956;
Graustein, Rhodora 58: 20–22, 1956.
Cronquist, Rhodora 59: 100, 1957.

340. *Panicum* L., Gen. Pl., ed. 5, 29, 1754; Sp. Pl. 55, 1753.
See Hitchcock & Chase, U. S. Natl. Herb., Contr. 15: 11–
16, 1910.

341. *Klibea* Sherff, Field Mus. Nat. Hist., Bot Ser. 8(6): 423,
1932.

342. *Callicarpa resinosa* Wright & Moldenke, Fedde Repert. Sp.
Nov. 33: 142–143, 1933.

C. resinosa Wright & Moldenke ex Moldenke, Fedde Repert.
Sp. Nov. 40: 77–78, 1936.

343. *Nani*(a) *lutea* (Gray) Heller, Minn. Bot. Stud. 1: 867–868,
1897.

Metrosideros lutea Gray, Bot. U. S. Expl. Exped. 15: 560,
1854.

Nani Adans., Fam. Pl. 2: 88, 1763.

Nania Miq., Fl. Ind. Bat. 1(1): 399, 1855.

Metrosideros Banks ex Gaertn., Fruct. 1: 170, pl. 34, fig. 1,
1788.

344. *Phyllites* Brongn., Mus. Hist. Nat. Paris, Mém. 8: 237–238,
1822.

Quercus mohavensis Axelrod, Carnegie Inst. Wash., Publ.
516: 99, pl. 8, fig. 1, 1939.

Phyllitis dentatus Axelrod, Carnegie Inst. Wash., Publ.
516: 128, pl. 12, fig. 9, 1939.
See Lamotte, Geol. Soc. Am., Mem. 51: 294, 1952.

345. *Oxalis Wrightii* Gray, Pl. Wright., in Smithsonian Inst.,
Contr. Know. 3(5): 27, 1850.

346. *Alisma Damasonium* L., Sp. Pl. 343, 1753.
Damasonium Alisma Mill., Gard. Dict. ed. 8, Alisma No. 1,
1768.
Damasonium damasonium (L.) Aschers. & Graebn., Fl.
Mitteleurop. 1: 389, 1897.
D. Stellatum Thuill., Fl. Paris, ed. 2, 186, 1799.

347. *Bicornes* L., Gen. Pl., ed. 6, sixth page after the index,
1764.
See H. F. Copeland, Madroño 9: 65, 96, 1947.

348. *Aciphylla* J. R. & G. Forst., Char. Gen. 135–136, pl. 68,
1776.
Laserpitium Aciphylla (J. R. & G. Forst.) Forst. f., Fl. Ins.
Aust. Prodr. 22, 1786.

349. *Holcus* L., Gen. Pl. 469, 1754; Sp. Pl. 1,047–1,049, 1753.
See Hitchcock, Gen. Grasses U. S., U. S. Dept. Agric.,
Bul. 772: 266, 1920; Man. Grasses U. S., U. S.
Dept. Agric., Misc. Publ. 200: ed. 2, 957, 1950;
Shinners, Baileya 4: 141–142, 1956.

350. *Urophyllum Johannis Winkleri* Merr., Inst. Allgem. Bot.
Hamburg, Mitt. 7(4): 289–290, 1937.

351. *Potamogeton Purshii* Tuckerm., Am. Jour. Sci. II, 6: 228,
1848.

352. *Hedysarum Macquenzii* Richards. forma *canescens*
Fedtschenko, Hort. Petrop., Acta 19: 274, 1901.
H. Mackenzii Richards. var. *canescens* Fedtschenko, Hort.
Petrop., Acta 19: 362, 1901.
H. Mackenzii Hook., Fl. Bor.-Am. 1: 155–156, 1831.
H. boreale Nutt. var. *cinerascens* (Rydb.) Rollins, Rhodora
42: 234, 1940.
H. cinerascens Rydb., New York Bot. Gard., Mem. 1: 257,
1900.

353. *Pinus baumani* Read, Carnegie Inst. Wash., Publ. 416: 11–
12, 1933.
P. bowmanii Read, Carnegie Inst. Wash., Publ. 416: pl. 3,
fig. 1–6, 1933.
See Lamotte, Geol. Soc. Am., Mem. 51: 253, 1952.

354. *Pandanus Hermsianus* Martelli, Univ. Calif. Publ. Bot.
13(7): 145–146, pl. 12, 1926.
P. fanningensis Martelli, Roy. Soc. Queensland, Proc.
45(4): 23, 1933.
P. spiralis R. Br., Prodr. 341, 1810.

355. *Fouilloya* Gaud., Bot. Voy. La Bonite, pl. 26, fig. 1–7, 21–
24, (1844–1866) = [1841].

356. *Viorna* (Spach) Gray, Syn. Fl. N. Am. 1(1): 5, 1895.
Viorna Pers. in Reichb., Handb. Natürlich. Pflanzensyst.
277, 1837.
Viorna Pers., Syn. Pl. 2: 98, 1807.
Urnigerae Lavalée, Clematites Gr. Fl. 47, 1884.
See Erickson, Mo. Bot. Gard., Ann. 30: 12, 1943.

357. *Arum Colocasia* L., Sp. Pl. 965, 1753.
Colocasia Antiquorum Schott in Schott & Endl., Meletem.
Bot. 1: 18, 1832.
Caladium Colocasia (L.) W. F. Wight, U. S. Natl. Herb.,
Contr. 9: 208, 1905.
Arum esculentum L., Sp. Pl. 965, 1753.
Caladium esculentum (L.) Vent., Descr. Pl. Nouv. Jard.
Cels. pl. 30, 1800; Willd. in Linnaeus, Sp. Pl., ed. 4 by
Willd. 4: 489, 1805.
Colocasia antiquorum Schott var. ε *esculenta* (L.) Schott,
Syn. Aroid. 42, 1856.
Colocasia esculenta (L.) Schott in Schott & Endl., Meletem.
Bot. 1: 18, 1832; Engler in DC., Monogr. Phan. 2: 491,
1879.
Colocasia esculenta (L.) Schott var. *typica* A. F. Hill, Har-
vard Univ., Bot. Mus., Leafl. 7(7): 116, 1939.

358. *Eggelingia* Summerh., Harvard Univ. Bot. Mus., Leafl.
14(9): 235–236, 1951.

359. *Puccinia Polygoni amphibii* Pers., Syn. Meth. Fung. 227–
228, 1801.
Uredo Polygoni Schum., Pl. Saell. 2: 233, 1803.
Puccinia Polygoni Alb. & Schw., Consp. Fung. 127, 1805.
Dicaeoma Polygoni-amphibii (Pers.) Arth., Ind. Acad. Sci.,
Proc. 1898: 184, 1899.
See Jackson, Mycologia 19: 55, 1927.

360. *Dalechampia* [Plum.] L., Gen. Pl., ed. 5, 473, 1754.

361. *Hysterium smilacis* Schw., Naturf. Ges. Leipzig, Schr. 1:
49, 1822; Schw. in Fries, Syst. Mycol. 2(2): 586, 1823.

Hysterographium smilacis (Schw.) Ellis & Everh., N. Am.
Pyren. 709, 1892.

Gloniopsis smilacis (Schw.) Underw. & Earle, Ala. Agric.
Exp. Sta., Bul. 80: 196, 1897.

G. Ellisii Cash, Mycologia 31: 294, 1939.

Hypoderma smilacis (Schw.) Sacc., Syll. Fung. 10: 789,
1883.

Hypodermopsis smilacis (Schw.) Cash, Mycologia 31: 293,
1939.

See Petrak, Sydowia 6: 290-292, 1952.

362. *Lupinus Hellerae* Heller, Torrey Bot. Club, Bul. 25: 265,
1898.

L. minimus Dougl. var. *Hellerae* (Heller) C. P. Sm. & St.
John in St. John, Fl. S. E. Wash. 228, 1937.

L. Helleri Greene, Pittonia 4: 134, 1900.

363. *Platyzomataceae* Nakai, Natl. Sci. Mus. Tokyo, Bul. 29: 4,
1950.

364. *Sagittaria calycina* Engelm. in Torr., Mex. Bound. Surv. Bot.
2: 212, (1858) =[1859].

Lophiocarpus calycinus (Englem.) Micheli in DC., Monogr.
Phan. 3: 61-62, 1881.

Lophiocarpus Turcz., Soc. Imp. Nat. Moscou, Bul. 16: 55,
1843.

Lophotocarpus calycinus (Engelm.) J. G. Sm., Mo. Bot.
Gard., Rept. 6: 60, 1895.

Lophianthus calycinus (Engelm.) Micheli ex J. G. Sm.,
Torrey Bot. Club, Mem. 5: 25, 1894.

365. *Agavoideae* Pax in Engler & Prantl, Nat. Pflanzenfam. IV,
2(5): 115, 1887.

Agaveae Endl., Gen. Pl. 181, 1836-1840.

Agavaceae Lotsy, Vorträge Bot. Stammesgesch. 3: 806,
1911.

366. *Corydalis aurea* Willd., Enum. Hort. Reg. Bot. Berol. 2:
740, 1809.

Fumaria aurea Mühl. in Willd., Enum. Hort. Reg. Bot. Berol.
2: 740, 1809.

C. aurea Willd. var. α *typica* Regel, Acad. Imp. Sci. St.
Petersb., Mém. VII, 4: 19, 1861.

C. aurea Willd. ssp. *aurea* Ownbey, Mo. Bot. Gard., Ann.
34: 229, 1947.

367. *Succuta* (Des Moulins) Yuncker, Illinois Biol. Monogr.
6(2-3): 21, 1921.

Eucuscuta Engelm., Acad. Sci. St. Louis, Trans. 1: 460,
1859.

Súccuta Des Moulins, Études Org. Cusc. 74, pl. 17, 1853.

Schrebera L., Sp. Pl., ed. 2, 1,662, 1763.

Lepimenes Raf., Fl. Tellur. 4: 91, 1836.

368. *Cyrtandra Wilderi* St. John & Storey, Bishop Mus., Occ. Pap.
20(6): 88, 1950.

C. Lessoniana Gaud. var. β Hbd., Fl. Haw. Is. 331, 1888.

C. Lessoniana Gaud. var. *stenoloba* Skottsb., Göteborg Bot.
Trädgård, Med. 10: 173, 1936.

369. *Conyza Japonica* (Thunb.) Less., Syn. Gen. Composit. 204,
1832; DC., Prodr. 5: 382, 1836.

Erigeron Japonicum Thunb., Fl. Jap. 312-313, 1784.

370. *Elymus mollis* Trin. in Spreng., Neu. Entd. 2: 72, 1821.

E. arenarius L. β *villosus* E. Mey., Pl. Labrad. 20, 1830.

E. ampliculmis Provanch., Fl. Canad. 2: 706, 1862.

E. capitatus Scribn., U. S. Dept. Agric., Div. Agrost., Bul.
11: 55, pl. 14, 1898.

E. arenarius L., Sp. Pl. 83, 1753.

E. dives Presl, Rel. Haenk. 1: 265, 1830.

E. arenarius L. ssp. *mollis* (Trin.) Hultén, Kungl. Svenska
Vetenskapsakad., Handl. III, 5(1): 153-155, 1927.

See St. John, Rhodora 17: 98-103, 1915.

Hitchcock, U. S. Dept. Agric., Misc. Publ. 200: 249,
845, 1935.

Löve, Soc. Fauna & Fl. Fennica, Acta 72(15): 6,
1955.

371. *Plectocomiopsis dubius* Becc., Roy, Bot. Gard. Calcutta,
Ann. 12(2): 56, 58, pl. 37, 1918.

372. *Melicocca* L., Sp. Pl., ed. 2, 495, 1763.
Melicoccus P. Br., Civ. Nat. Hist. Jam. 210–211, 1756.
See Taxon 3: 241, 1954.

373. *Ficus velascoi* (Merr.) Sata, Monogr. Stud. Ficus, Taihoku
Imp. Univ., Fac. Agric., Inst. Hort. & Econ. Bot.,
Contr. 32(1): 242, 275, 1944.

374. *Panax Schin-seng* Nees, Icon. Pl. Med. Suppl. No. 70, fasc.
5, pl. 16, unnumbered, 1833.
P. Ginseng C. A. Meyer, Repert. Pharm. Chem., Jahrg.
1842(8): 524, 1842; Phys. Math. Acad. St. Petersburg,
Bul. 1: 340, 1843.
Aralia Ginseng (C. A. Meyer) Baill., Hist. Pl. 7: 197, 1880.
See Hill, Harvard Univ. Bot. Mus., Leafl. 10: 163, 1942.

375. *Betula Andrewsii* A. Nels., Bot. Gaz. 43: 279–281, 1907.
B. papyrifera Andrewsii (A. Nels.) F. P. Daniels, Univ.
Mo. Stud., Sci. Ser. 2: 101, 1911.
B. occidentalis Hook. ×*papyrifera* Marsh., Froiland, Evolu-
tion 6(3): 281, 1952.
See Butler, Torrey Bot. Club, Bul. 36: 435, 1909.

376. ×*Veronicena* Moldenke, Phytologia 5: 133, 1955.
×*V.* ×*Haartmani* Moldenke, Phytologia 5: 134, 1955.
Veronica×*hybrida* Haartm., Pl. Hybrid. 7–8, 1751.
Veronica hybrida L., Sp. Pl. 11, 1753.
Veronica ×*spuria* Haartm., Amoen. Acad. 3: 35, pl. 2, 1756.
Veronica spuria L., Sp. Pl. 10, 1753.

377. *Larix laricina* (Du Roi) K. Koch, Dendrol. 2(2): 263, 1873.
Pinus Laricina Du Roi, Dissert. Inaug. Observ. Bot. 49–50,
[1771].

378. *Platycarya* Sieb. & Zucc., Akad. Muenchen, Abh. 3(3): 741–
743, pl. 5, fig. 1, 1843.
Petrophiloides Bowerbank, Foss. Fr. London Clay 43, 1840.

379. *Syzygium* Gaertn., Fruct. 1: 166, 1788.
Suzygium Gaertn., Fruct. 3: pl. 33, fig. 1, 1788.

380. *Corynocarpus* J. R. & G. Forst., Char. Gen. 31–32, pl. 16,
1776.

381. *Barleria* [Plum.] ex L., Gen. Pl., ed. 5, 283, 1754.

382. *Panicum Mattamusketense* Ashe, Elisha Mitchell Sci. Soc.,
     Jour. 15: 45, 1898.

383. *Horsfieldia* Willd., Sp. Pl. of Linnaeus, ed. 4 by Willd., 4:
     872, 1805.
     Horkelia C. & S., Linnaea 2: 26, 1827.

384. *Rooseveltia* O. F. Cook, Smithsonian Misc. Coll. 98(7):
     21-22, pl. 1-19, 1939.

385. *Aesculus* L., Gen. Pl., ed. 5, 500, 1754; Sp. Pl. 344, 1753.
     Esculus L., Gen. Pl., ed. 5, 161, 1754.
     Oesculus Neck., Elem. Bot. 2: 232, 1790.

386. *Cyrtandra lillianae* Setchell in Wilder, Bishop Mus., Bul. 86:
     98, fig. 3, 1931.

387. *Euodia* Bailey ex Pritch., Hist. Infusoria 852, 1861.
     Euodia Gaertn., Fruct. 2: pl. 103, fig. 2, 1791.
     Euodia J. R. & G. Forst., Char. Gen. 13, pl. 72, 1776.
     Evodea Kunth, Syn. Pl. 3: 327, 1824.
     Evodia Gaertn., Fruct. 2: 100, pl. 103, 1791.

388. *Scolecotrichum Asclepiadis* Ellis & Everh., Erythea 1: 203,
     1893.

389. *Thermopsis pauciflora* Thornber ex Larisey, Mo. Bot. Gard.,
     Ann. 27: 252, 1940.

390. *Melochia concatenata* L., Sp. Pl. 675, 1753.
     M. corchorifolia L., Sp. Pl. 675, 1753.
         See Mast. in Hook. f., Fl. Brit. India 1: 374, 1874.
         Merrill, Am. Phil. Soc., Trans. 24(2): 264, 1935.

391. *Sassafras variifolium* (Salisb.) Ktze., Rev. Gen. Pl. 2: 574,
     1891.
     Laurus Variifolia Salisb., Prodr. Hort. Chap. Allerton 344,
     1796.
     Laurus Sassafras L., Sp. Pl. 371, 1753.
     Laurus albida Nutt., Gen. N. Am. Pl. 1: 259-260, 1818.
     Tetranthera albida (Nutt.) Spreng., Syst. Veg. of Linnaeus,
     ed. 16 by Spreng., 2: 267, 1825.
     Sassafras officinalis Nees & Eberm., Handb. Med.-Pharm.
     Bot. 2: 418, 1831.
     S. albidum (Nutt.) Nees, Syst. Laurin. 490, 1836.
     S. triloba Raf., Autikon Bot. 85, 1840.

S. *Sassafras* (L.) Karst., Deut. Fl. Pharm.-Med. Bot. 505, (1882) = [1881].

S. *albidum* var. *molle* (Raf.) Fern., Rhodora 38: 179, 1936.

S. *variifolium* (Salisb.) Ktze. var. *albidum* (Nutt.) Fern., Rhodora 15: 16, 1913.

S. *albida* (Nutt.) Nees var. *glauca* Nieuwl., Am. Midl. Nat. 3: 347, 1914.

S. *officinale* Nees & Eberm. var. *albidum* (Nutt.) Blake, Rhodora 20: 99, 1918.

392. *Verrucaria* Webber ex Wiggers, Prim. Fl. Holsat. 85, 1780.

Verrucariomyces Thomas ex Cif. & Tom., Inst. Bot. Lab. Crittog. Pavia, Atti V, 10: 31, 1952; Thomas, Beitr. Kryptogamenfl. Schweiz 9(1): 171, 1939.

393. *Swertia* L., Gen. Pl., ed. 5, 107, 1754; Sp. Pl. 226–227, 1753.

Svertia L., Sp. Pl. index, 1753.

394. *Poa amboinica* L., Mant. Alt. 557, 1771.

Phoenix amboinica montana Rumph., Herb. Amboin. 6: 19, pl. 7, fig. 3, 1750.

Andropogon amboinicus (L.) Merr., Interpret. Rumph. Herb. Amboin. 88, 1917.

See Fischer, Kew. Bul. 398–400, 1934.

Airy Shaw, H. K., Kew Bul. 36, 1947.

Furtado, Gardens' Bul. 9: 246, 1937.

395. *Pisum maritimum* L. β *glabrum* Ser. in DC., Prodr. 2: 368, 1825.

Lathyrus japonicus Willd. var. *glaber* (Ser.) Fern., Rhodora 34: 181, 1932.

396. *Quercus Margaretta* Ashe in Small, Fl. S. E. U. S. 355, 1903; ed. 2, 355, 1913.

Q. minor (Marsh.) Sarg. var. *Margaretta* Ashe, Elisha Mitchell Sci. Soc., Jour. 11: 94, 1894.

Q. stellata Wang. var. *Margaretta* (Ashe) Sarg., Trees & Shrubs 2: 219, pl. 185, 1913.

397. *Eugenia waianensis* Degener, Fl. Haw. 273: with figure, 7/15/'32.

E. rariflora Benth. var. *parvifolia* Hbd., Fl. Haw. Is. 129, 1888.

E. parvifolia DC., Prodr. 3: 266, 1828.

398. *Dentaria digitata* Lam., Encyc. Méth. Bot. 2: 268, 1786.

Cardamine hyperborea O. E. Schulz, Engl. Bot. Jahrb. 32: 550, 1903.

C. Richardsonii Hultén, Lunds Univ., Årssk. 41: 838, 1945.

C. digitata Richards. in Franklin, Journey Shores Polar Sea, Bot. Append. 743, 1823.

See Rollins, Rhodora 54: 260, 1952.

399. *Quercus Lowilliamsi* Muller, Madroño 10: 138–139, pl. 11, 1950.

400. *Pithecellobium* Mart., in v. Schrank & Mart., Hort. Reg. Monac. 188, 1829.

Pithecollobium Mart., Flora 20(2), Beibl: 114, 1837.

Zygia P. Browne, Civ. Nat. Hist. Jamaica 279, pl. 22, fig. 3, 1789.

Zygia Boehm. ed. Ludw., Def. Gen. Pl. 72, 1760.

Siderocarpus Small, New York Bot. Gard., Bul. 2: 91, 1901.

Havardia Small, New York Bot. Gard., Bul. 2: 91–92, 1901.

Ebenopsis Britton & Rose, N. Am. Fl. 23(1): 33, 1928.

401. *Epidendrum Flos aëris* L., Sp. Pl. 952, 1753.

402. *Cyrtandra Hosakae* St. John, Bishop Mus., Occas. Pap. 20(6): 82, 1950.

403. *Cyrtandra Lessoniana* Gaud., Bot. Voy. Freyc. Uranie 447, (1826) =[1829]; Atlas, pl. 54, 1826.

C. Lessoriana Gaud. sensu Wawra, Flora 30: 561 (reprint, p. 17), 1872.

404. *Coprosma ochracea* W. R. B. Oliver, var. *kaalae* St. John in W. R. B. Oliver, Bishop Mus., Bul. 132: 157–158, fig. 53, 1935.

405. *Leucanthemum* [Tourn.] Adans., Fam. Pl. 2: 127, 1763.

406. *Rosineae* Engler, Nat. Pflanzenfam., Nachtr. 349, 1897.

407. *Cyclospermum leptophyllum* (Pers.) Sprague, Jour. Bot. Brit. For. 61: 131, 1923.

Pimpinella leptophylla Pers., Syn. Pl. 1: 324, 1805.

Apium leptophyllum (Pers.) F. Muell. ex Benth., Fl. Austral. 3: 372, 1866.

Sison Ammi Jacq., Hort. Vindob. 2: 95, pl. 200, 1773.

Apium Ammi (L.) Urban, Fl. Bras. 11(1): 341, 1879.

See Constance in Kearney & Peebles, U. S. Dept. Agric.,
Misc. Publ. 423: 645, 1942.

408. *Eriosorus* Fée, Gen. Fil. 152, (1850–1852)=[1850].
See Pichi-Sermolli, Webbia 9: 361, 362, 1953.

409. *Oedogonium Kurzii* Zeller var. *ovatum* H. Silva, Torrey Bot.
Club. Bul. 80: 342–343, 1953.

410. *Conioselinum chinense* (L.) BSP., Prel. Cat. New York 22,
1888.
Athamanta chinensis L., Sp. Pl. 245, 1753.
Selinum canadense Michx., Fl. Bor.-Am. 1: 165, 1803.
Conioselinum ? canadense (Michx.) T. & G., Fl. N. Am. 1:
619, 1840.
See Hultén, Lunds Univ. Årsskr. n. f. II, 43(1): 1,175,
1946.

411. *Cupressus M'Nabiana* A. Murr., Edinb. New Phil. Jour. n.s.
1: 293, pl. 11, 1855; repr. 12–13, pl. 11, 1855.

412. *Sida pseudo-potentilloides* H. Monteiro f., Lilloa 17: 516,
1949.
S. potentilloides K. Schum. in Mart., Fl. Bras. 12(3): 334,
1891.
S. potentilloides St. Hil., Fl. Bras. Merid. 1: 110, 1825.

413. *Dioscorea sativa* L., Sp. Pl. 1,033, 1753.
D. sativa Thunb., Fl. Jap. 151, 1784.
D. bulbifera L. var. *sativa* Prain & Burkill, Calcutta Roy.
Bot. Gard., Ann. 14(1): 113, 117, 122–123, 132, 1936;
14(2): pl. 49–50, 1936.

414. *Urera sandwicensis* Wedd. γ *mollis* Wedd. in DC., Prodr.
16(1): 93, 1869.
U. glabra (H. & A.) Wedd. β *mollis* Wedd., Mus. Hist. Nat.
Paris, Arch. 9: 149, 1856.

415. × *Tritordeum* Aschers. & Graebn., Syn. Mitteleur. Fl. 2(1):
748, 1902.
× *Agroelymus* G. Camus in A. Camus, Mus. Natl. Hist. Nat.
Paris, Bul. 6: 538, 1927.
× *Elymopyrum* de Cugnac, Soc. Hist. Nat. Ardennes, Bul. 33:
1938.
Agropyron repens × *Elymus mollis* J. Adams, Can. Field
Nat. 50: 117, 1936.

×*Agroelymus Adamsii* Rousseau, Nat. Can. 69: 99, 1942.

×*Agroelymus jamesensis* Lepage var. *anticostensis* Lepage,
Nat. Can. 79: 247, 1952.

×*Agroelymus Adamsii* Rousseau, Jard. Bot. Montreal, Mem.
29: 16–20, 1952.

416. *Zygnema novae-caesareae* Habeeb, Rhodora 56: 41–42,
1954.
See Silva, Univ. Calif., Publ. Bot. 25: 253, 1952.

417. *Trifolium procumbens* L., Sp. Pl. 772–773, 1753.
T. filiforme L., Fl. Suec., ed. 2, 261–262, 1755.
T. dubium Sibth., Fl. Oxon. 231, 1794.
T. minus Sm. in Relhan, Fl. Cantabr., ed. 2, 290, 1802.
T. procumbens L., Fl. Suec., ed. 2, 261, 1755.
T. campestre Schreb. in Sturm, Deutschl. Fl. (1) heft. 16:
pl. 13 unpaged, 1804.
T. agrarium L., Fl. Suec., ed. 2, 261, 1755.
See Hermann, U. S. Dept. Agric., Agric. Monogr. 22: 11,
1954.

418. *Yucca glauca* Nutt., Fraser's Cat. 1813; repr. Pittonia 2:
119, 1890.
Y. angustifolia Pursh, Fl. Am. Sept. 1: 227, 1814.
See Shinners, Rhodora 57: 290–293, 1955;
Graustein, Rhodora 58: 20–22, 1956;
Cronquist *et al.,* Rhodora 58: 23–24, 1956;
Shinners, Rhodora 58: 281–289, 1956;
Cronquist, Rhodora 59: 100, 1957.

419. *Nummularia* Tul., Select. Fung. Carpolog. 2: 42–43, 1863.
Nummularia S. F. Gray, Nat. Arr. Brit. Pl. 2: 300, 1821.
Kommamyce Nieuwl., Am. Midl. Nat. 4: 375, 1916.

420. *Aralia* Necker, Elem. Bot. 1: 159, 1790.
Aralia [Tourn.] L., Gen. Pl., ed. 5, 134, 1754.

421. *Anthoceros megalospermus* Gottsche, Bot. Zeit. 16,
Beilage: 19, 1858.
A. megalosporus Gottsche, Bot. Zeit. 16, Beilage: 48, 1858.

422. *Hypnomonas pleiopyrenigerum* Moewus, Bot. Notis. 1953:
406–409, fig. 3, 1953.

423. *Anthoceros Havaiensis* Reichardt, K. K. Wien Akad.,
Sitzungsber, Abt. 1, 75: 562, 1877.

A. hawaiensis Reich. ex Stephani, Herb. Boiss., Bul. 5:
841, 1897.

Aspiromitus hawaicus (Reich.) Steph., Sp. Hepat. 5: 967,
1916.

424. *Liabum (Sinclairia) columbianum* Klatt, Engl. Bot. Jahrb.
8: 47, 1887.

Gynoxys columbiana (Klatt) Hieron., Engl. Bot. Jahrb. 28:
631, 1901.

G. columbian (Klatt) Hieron. ex Cuatr., Fieldiana, Bot.
27(2): 17, 1951.

425. *Aster arcticus* Rupp., Fl. Ienensis 144, 1726.

426. *Galapagoa* Hook f., Linn. Soc. Lond., Proc. 1: 277, (1849) =
[1845].

427. *Spirotecoma* Baill., Hist. Pl. 10: 49, 1891.

428. *Migandra* O. F. Cook, Natl. Hort. Mag. (Am.) 22: 142 in
obs., 152, 1943.

429. *Melaleuca Leucadendra* (L.) L., Mant. Pl. 1: 105, 1767.

Myrtus Leucadendra Stickm., Herb. Amb. 9, 1754; Amoen.
Acad. 4: 120, 1759.

Myrtus Leucadendra L., Syst. Nat., ed. 10, 2: 1,056, 1759.

Melalevca Leucadendra (L.) L., Syst. Nat., ed. 13, 2: 509,
1770.

Melaleuca Leucadendron (L.) L. ex L. f., Suppl. Pl. 342,
1781.

See Little, Check List Nat. Nat. Trees U. S., U. S. Dept.,
Agric., For. Serv. 160, 1944; U. S. Dept. Agric.,
Agric. Handbook 41: 239, 1953.

430. *Aspergillus mangini* (Mangin) Thom & Raper, Manual
Aspergilli 127, 1945.

Eurotium herbariorum Link ser. *minor* Mangin, Ann. Sci.
Nat. Bot. IX, 10: 366–370, 1909.

A. minor (Mangin) Thom & Raper, U. S. Dept. Agric., Misc.
Publ. 426: 27–29, 1941.

Sterigmatocystis minor Bainier, Soc. Bot. France, Bul. 27:
30–31, 1880.

431. *Amphoradenium haalilioanum* (Brack.) Copel., Gen. Fil. 220,
1947.

Polypodium Haalilioanum Brack., U. S. Expl. Exped. Bot.
16: 5-6, 1854; Atlas 16: pl. 1, fig. 4, 1854.

P. subpinnatifidum (Bl.) Hook., Sp. Fil. 4: 177, 1862.

Grammitis subpinnatifidum (Bl.) Bl., Fil. Jav. 118, pl. 49,
fig. 2, 1830.

P. subpinnatifidum Bl., Enum. Pl. Jav. 129, 1827.

432. Cuphea P. Browne, Civ. Nat. Hist. Jamaica 216, 1756.

Balsamona Vand., Fasc. Pl. 15, 1771.

Dipetalon Raf., Sylva Tellur. 103, 1838.

Duvernaya Desp. in DC., Prodr. 3: 86, 1828.

433. *Xylaria Cornu Dorcas* Lloyd, Myc. Writ. 7: 1,206, pl. 249,
fig. 2,498, 1924.

X. cornu dorcas Lloyd emend. Stevenson & Cash, Lloyd
Libr. & Mus., Bul. 35 (Mycol. Ser. 8): 13, 1936.

434. Schadjaret elharneb Forsk., Fl. Aegypt. Arab. 195, 1775.

435. *Kosaria* Forsk., Fl. Aegypt. Arab. 164-165, 1775.

436. *Stephanospermum stewarti* J. W. Hall, Bot. Gaz. 115: 354-
356, fig. 21-28, 1954.

437. *Volvox capensis* Pocock, S. Afr. Mus., Ann. 16(3): 441-447,
repr., n. d.

438. *Verbena litoralis* HBK., Nov. Gen. et Sp. Pl. 2: 276, pl.
137, 1817.

Senecio littoralis Gaud., Ann. Sci. Nat. I, 5: 104, 1825.

Ranunculus litoralis Phil., Linnaea 28: 663, 1856.

Carex littoralis Schwein., Lyc. New York, Ann. 1: 70, 1824.

439. *Budleia* Houston ex Adanson, Fam. Pl. 2: 224, 1763.

Budleja L., Gen. Pl., ed. 1, 1: index, 1737; 2: 95, and index, 1737.

Buddleja Houston ex L., Hort. Cliffort. 35, 1737; Gen. Pl.,
ed. 1, 1: 26, 1737; ed. 5, 51, 1754; ed. 6, 57, 1764; Sp.
Pl. ed. 1, 112, 1753; Syst. Nat. of Linnaeus, ed. 12 by
Beckmann, 2: 56, index, 1772.

Buddleia L., Syst. Nat., ed. 13, 2: 121, index, 1770; Benth.
in DC., Prodr. 10: 433, 436, 1846; B. & H., Gen. Pl.
2(2); 793, 1876; Solereder in Engler & Prantl, Nat.
Pflanzenfam. 4(2): 47, 1897.

Buddlea L., ex Spreng. in Syst. Veg. of Linnaeus, ed. 16
by Spreng. 1: 428, 975, 1825.

Buddleya L. ex Franch. & Savat., Enum. Pl. Jap. 1: 322, 1874.

Budlaea Sw., Observ. Bot. 47, 1791.

Budlea L. ex St. Hil., Expos. Fam. Nat. Pl. 1: 272, 1805.
See Nakai, Natl. Sci. Mus. (Tokyo), Bul. 29: 73, 1950.
Rickett, Taxon 4: 185–188, 1955.

440. *Peckifungus* Ktze., Rev. Gen. Pl. 2: 864, 1891.

441. *Candida* Berkh., De Schlimmelg. Monilia 41, 1923.

442. *Dendrophthora Willtreleasii* Stehlé, Soc. Bot. France, Bul. (Mem. 1953–1954): 32, 1954.

443. *Jungermannia trichophylla* L., Sp. Pl. 1,135, 1753.
Blepharostoma trichophyllum (L.) Dumort., Rec. d'Obs. 18, 1835.

444. *Hypnum Stereodon virginianus* Brid., Bryol. Univ. 2: 576, 1827.

445. *Isotoma runcinata* Hassk., Bonplandia 7: 181–183, 1859.
Laurentia longiflora (L.) Endl. var. *runcinata* (Hassk.) E. Wimm., Nat. Hist. Mus. Wien, Ann. 56: 337, 1948.

446. *Saxo-fridericia* Schomb., Rapat. Frid.-Aug. Braunschw. 13, pl. 2, 1845.

447. *Nostoc* Paracelsus ex S. F. Gray, Nat. Arr. Brit. Pl. 1: 351, 1821.
Nostoch Paracelsus, Sämtliche Werke, ed. J. Strebel 8: 488, 1949.
Nostoc Vaucher, Histoire des conferves d'eau douce 203, 1803.
Nostoc Vaucher ex Born. & Flah., Ann. Sci. Nat. Bot. VII, 7: 181–183, 1888.
Tremella Nostoc L., Sp. Pl., ed. 2, 1,625, 1763.

448. *Phyllites kaiwakaensis* McQueen, Roy. Soc. N. Z., Trans. 82(3): 676, pl. 27, fig. 6, 1954.

449. *Notonia* Wight & Arn., Prodr. Fl. Penins. Ind. Orient. 1: 207–208, 1834.
Notonia DC., Guillemin's Archives de Bot. 2: 518, 1833.
Johnia Wight & Arn., Prodr. Fl. Penins. Ind. Orient. 1: 449, 1834.

450. *Pandanus spurius* Rumph., Herb. Amb. 4: 142–143, pl. 75, 1750.

P. *spurius* (Martelli) Rumph, Webbia 4(1): 31, 1913.

P. *spurius* Miq., Anal. Bot. Ind. 2: 27, 1851.

P. *spurius* Kurz, Jour. Bot. Brit. For. 5: 129, 1867.

P. *spurius* Rumph. ex Martelli, Soc. Bot. Ital., Bul. 299, 1904; repr. 2, 1904.

451. *Brachycome* superspecies *leptocarpa B. uliginosa* G. L. Davis, Linn. Soc. N. S. W., Proc. 79: 203–204, fig. 1–4, 1955.

452. *Cercospora platyspora* Ellis & Holway, Jour. Mycol. 3: 16, 1887.

Fusicladium depressum v. Hoehnel, Ann. Mycol. 1: 531, 1903.

See Chupp, Monogr. Fung. Gen. Cercospora 578, (1953) = [1954].

453. *Lophostigma* Brongn., Ann. Sci. Nat. Bot. VI, 1: 286, 1875.

Lophostigma (Brongn.) Warb., Engler's Pflanzenreich IV, 9: 44, 71, 1900.

454. *Eusabatia* Griseb., Gen. et Sp. Gent. 120, 1839.

Eusabatia (Griseb.) Blake, Rhodora 17: 56, 1915.

See Wilbur, Rhodora 57: 5, 1955.

455. *Pandanus saipanensis* Kanehira, Jour. Jap. Bot. (Shokubutsu Kenkyu Zasshi) 12: 549, fig. 16–17, 1936.

P. *saipanensis* Kanehira, Bot. Mag. [Tokyo] 50: 521–522, fig. 43–44, 1936.

456. *Pithecellobium monopterum* Kostermans, New & Crit. Malaysian Pl. 2: 1–3, fig. 1, 1954; Reinwardtia 3: 1–3, fig. 1, 1954.

457. *Sida acuta* Burm. f., Fl. Ind. 147, 1768.

Silagurium longifolia Rumph., Herb. Amboin. 6: 45–46, pl. 18, fig. 2, 1750.

Tsjeru-parua Rheede, Hort. Malabar. 10: 105, pl. 53, 1686.

458. *Tulasnella metallica* Rick, Broteria Ciênc. Nat. 3: 169, 1934.

Ceratobasidium plumbeum Martin, Mycologia 31: 513. fig. 21–27, 1939.

C. atratum (Bres.) Rogers ex Martin, Lloydia 4: 262, 1941.
Corticium atratum Bres., Hedwigia 35: 290, 1896.
   See Univ. Iowa Nat. Hist. Stud. 17: 31, 1935;
      Rogers & Jackson, Farlowia 1: 272, 1943.

459. *Asplenium Trich. dentatum* L., Sp. Pl. 1,080, 1753.
   A. dentatum L., Syst. Nat., ed. 10, 2: 1,323, 1759.
   A. barbadense Jenman, Gard. Chron. III, 15: 134, 1894.

460. *Wikströmia* Spreng., Svensk. Vet. Akad, Stockholm, Handl.
      III, 9: 167, 1821.
   Wickstroemia Endl., Prodr. Fl. Norfolk 47, 1833.
   Capura Blanco, Fl. Filip. 264 (error typ. 644), 1837.
   Diplomorpha Meissn., K. Bayerische Bot. Gesell. Regens-
      burg, Denkschr. 3: 289, 1841.
   D. elongata recurva (Hbd.) Heller, Geol. & Nat. Hist. Surv.
      Minn. 9: (Minn. Bot. Stud. 1:) 859–860, 1897.
   Capura L., Mant. Alt. 149, 1771.

CHAPTER 5

500. *Vitex trifolia* L. var. α *trifoliolata* Schauer in DC., Prodr.
11: 683, 1847.

V. trifolia L. α *trifoliata* Cham., Linnaea 7: 107, 1832.
See Lam, H. J., Verbenaceae of Malayan Archip. 182,
1919.

501. *Scirpus lateralis* Forsk., Fl. Aegypt. Arab. 15, 1775.

S. lateriflorus Gmel., Syst. Nat. of Linnaeus, ed. 13 reform.
by Gmel., 2(1): 127, 1796.

S. lateralis Retz., Obs. Bot. 4: 12, 1786.

S. erecto-gracilis Hayata, Icon. Pl. Formosa 6: 114, fig. 31,
1916.

Isolepis uninodis Delile, Fl. Aegypt. 8–9, pl. 6, fig. 1,
1812.

S. uninodis (Delile) Boiss., Fl. Orient. 5: 380, 1884.

S. uninodis (Delile) Boiss. ex Beetle, Am. Jour. Bot. 29:
656, 1942.

S. erectus Poir. in Lam., Encyc. Méth. Bot. 6: 761, 1804.
See Christensen, Dansk. Bot. Arkiv 4: 12, 1922.

Blake, S. T., Roy. Soc. Queensland, Proc. 62: 83–88,
1952.

502. *Hoya esculenta* (Rumph.) Tsiang, Sunyatsenia 3: 176, 1936.

Sussuela esculentum Rumph., Herb. Amb. 5: 467–468, pl.
175, fig. 2, 1750.

Hoya diversifolia Bl., Bijd. Fl. Nederl. Ind. 1,064, 1825.

H. orbiculata Wall. ex Wight, Contr. Bot. Ind. 36, 1834.
See Furtado, Gardens' Bul. 12: 372, 1949.

503. *Hemerocallis Lilio Asphodelus* L., Sp. Pl. 324, 1753.

H. flava L., Sp. Pl., ed. 2, 1: 462, 1763.

504. *Pseudotsuga glaucescens* (Roezl) Bailly, Rev. Hort. (Paris)
67: 88–90, col. pl., 1895.

Abies glaucescens Roezl, Cat. Grain. Conif. Mex. 1858–
1859: 5, 1858; Linnaea 29: 330, 1858.

Picea glaucescens (Roezl) Gordon, Pinetum 149, 1858.

A. religiosa (HBK.) Schlecht. & Cham. var. *glaucescens*
(Roezl) Carr., Traité Gén. Conif., nouv. ed. 274, 1867.

Pseudotsuga taxifolia (Poir.) Britton ex Sudw. var. *glauca*
(Beissn.) Schneid. forma *glaucescens* Schneid. in
Silva Tarouca, Uns. Freil.-Nadelh. 269, 1913.

505. *Gelidium samoense* Reinbold forma *lineare* Setchell, Univ.
Calif. Publ. Bot. 12: 99, 1926.

G. samoense Reinbold forma *minus* Setchell, Carnegie
Inst. Wash., Publ. 341: 163, 1924.

See Taxon 3: 234, 1954; 4: 118, 1955.

506. *Brugmansia arborea* (Pers.) Steud., Nomencl., ed. 2, 230,
484, 1841.

507. *Cystopteris montana* (Lam.) Bernh. ex Desv., Prodr. 264,
1827.

Polypodium montanum Lam., Fl. Fr. 1: 23, 1778.

Cyathea montana (Lam.) Sm., Acad. Roy. Sci. Turin, Mem. 5:
417, 1793.

Aspidium montanum (Lam.) Sw. in Schrad. Jour. 1800(2):
42–43, 1801.

Athyrium montanum Spreng., Anleit. Kenntn. Gewächse 3:
143, 1804.

Filix montana Underw., Our Nat. Ferns, ed. 6, 119, 1900.

Filicula montana (Lam.) Farw., Am. Midl. Nat. 12: 252,
1931.

Filicula Sequier, Pl. Veron., Suppl. 3: 54–55, tab. 1, 1754.

508. *Peniophora admirabilis* Burt, Mo. Bot. Gard., Ann. 12: 304,
(1925) = [1926].

See Rogers & Jackson, Farlowia 1: 310, 1943.

509. *Dubautia raillardioides* Hbd., Fl. Haw. Is. 224, 1888.

Railliardia Gaud., Voy. Freycinet, Uranie, Bot. 469, pl. 83,
(1826) = [1830].

Dubautia Railliardioides Hbd. emend. Sherff, Bishop Mus.,
Bul. 135: 107, 1935.

510. *Asclepias syriaca* L., Sp. Pl. 214, 1753.

Apocynum syriacum Clus., Rar. Pl. Hist. 5: lxxxviii, 1601.

511. *Heracleum maximum* W. Bartr., Travels 344, 1791; ed. 2,
        342, 1792; 342, 1794.
    H. lanatum Michx., Fl. Bor.-Am. 1: 166, 1803.
      See Fernald, Rhodora 46: 50, 1944.
         Rickett, Rhodora 46: 389–391, 1944.
         Merrill, Bartonia 23: 26, 1945.

512. *Musa Troglodylarum* L., Sp. Pl., ed. 2, 2: 1,478, 1763.
    M. Troglodytarum L., Sp. Pl., ed. 3, 2: 1,478, 1764.
    M. Uranoscopos Rumph., Herb. Amb. 5: 137, pl. 61, fig. 2,
        1750.
    M. Uranoscopus Colla, Accad. R. Sci. Torino, Mem. 25:
        387–388, 1820; repr. 59–60, 1820.
    M. Fehi Bert. ex Vieillard, Ann. Sci. Nat. Bot. IV, 16: 45,
        1862.
    M. Sapientum L. ssp. *M. Troglodytarum* (L.) L. ex Baker,
        Ann. Bot. 7: 214–215, 1893.
    M. paradisiaca L. ssp. *troglodytarum* (L.) Baker ex K.
        Schum. in Engler, Pflanzenreich IV, 45: 21, 1900.
    M. sapientum L. var. *M. troglodytarum* (L.) L. ex Anon.,
        Kew Bul. 250, 1894; Kew Bul., Add. Ser. 6: 22, 1906.

513. *Thelephora candida* Schw., Naturf. Ges. Leipzig, Schr. 1:
        110, 1822; Fr., Elench. Fung. 1: 189, 1828.
    T. candidissima Schw., Am. Phil. Soc., Trans. II, 4: 167,
        1832.
    Aleurodiscus candidus (Schw.) Burt, Mo. Bot. Gard., Ann.
        5: 188, 1918.
    T. (sub *Merisma*) *candida* (Schw.) Fr., Syst. Orb. Veg. 82,
        1825.
    Tremellodendron (sub *Merismate*) *candidum* (Schw.) Atk.,
        Jour. Mycol. 8: 106, 1902.

514. *Shorea costata* (Correa) J. S. Presl in Berchtold & J. S.
        Presl, Opřirozenosti rostlin 2: 66, 1825.
    Pterigium costatum Corréa de Serra, Mus. Hist. Nat. Paris,
        Ann. 8: 397–398, pl. 6, fig. 1, 1806.
    Dryobalanops aromatica Gaertn., Fruct. 4: 49, pl. 186, 1805.

515. *Heleocharis kasakstanica* Zinserl. in Komarov & Shischkin,
        Fl. U.R.S.S. 3: 78, 1935.

516. *Banksia* J. R. & G. Forst., Char. Gen. 7–8, pl. 4, 1776.
Pimelia Banks & Soland. ex Gaertn., Fruct. 1: 186, 1788.
Banksia L. f., Suppl. 15, 126, 1781.
Banksea Koen. in Retz., Obs. 3: 75, 1783.
Bankesia Bruce, Trav. Disc. Source Nile, ed. 2, 7: 181, 1805.
Banksia Bruce, Trav. Disc. Source Nile, ed. 2, 8: pl. 22–23, 1805.
Banksia Domb. ex DC., Prodr. 3: 83, 1828.

517. *Rubus rosaefolius* Sm., Pl. Icon. Ined. Herb. Linn. 3: pl. 60, 1791.
R. rosifolius Sm. emend. Hochr., Candollea 6: 464, 1936.
See Focke, Sp. Ruborum 153, 1910.

518. *Sclerotium bifrons* Ellis & Everh., N. Am. Fung. No. 2,554, 1891.
S. bifrons Ellis & Everh. in Sacc., Syll. Fung. 14: 1,169, 1899.
Sclerotinia bifrons Seaver & Shope, Mycologia 22: 3, pl., 1930.
Sclerotinia bifrons Whetzel, Mycologia 32: 126, 1940.
Sclerotinia confundens Whetzel, Mycologia 32: 126, 1940.
Sclerotinia Whetzelii Seaver, Mycologia 32: 127, 1940.
Ciborinia bifrons (Whetzel) Whetzel, Mycologia 37: 668, 1945.
Ciborinia confundens (Whetzel) Whetzel, Mycologia 37: 668, 1945.
Ciborinia Whetzelii (Seaver) Seaver, N. Am. Cup Fung. Inoper. 70, 1951.
Ciborinia bifrons (Ellis & Everh.) Seaver, N. Am. Cup Fung. Inoper. 71, 1951.

519. *Metrosideros collina* (J. R. & G. Forst.) Gray ssp. *polymorpha* (Gaud.) Rock var. *imbricata* Rock, Hawaii Board Agric. & For., Div. For., Bot. Bul. 4: 49, pl. 17, 1917.
M. polymorpha Gaud. ssp. *imbricata* Rock ex Skottsb., Göteborg Bot. Trädgård, Meddel. 15: 407, 1944.

520. *Morelotia gahniaeformis* Gaud., Bot. Voy. Frey. Uranie 416, (1826) = [1829]; Atlas pl. 28, 1826.

Gahnia gahniaeformis (Gaud.) Heller, Minn. Bot. Stud. 1:
    802, 1897.

Lampocarya Gaudichaudii Brongn. in Duperrey, Voy. Bot. 2:
    166, 1829.

G. Gaudichaudii (Brongn.) Steud., Syn. Pl. Glum. 2: 164,
    1855.

    See Benl, Bot. Archiv 40: 151–257, 1940.

521. *Apocynum fol. androsaemi* L., Sp. Pl. 213, 1753.

A. androsaemifolium L., Sp. Pl., ed. 2, 311, 1764.

A. androsaemifol. L., Syst. Nat., ed. 12 reform. 2: 192,
    1767.

A. androsaemi folium Mill., Gard. Dict., ed. 8, Apocynum
    No. 1, 1768.

A. androsaemifol. L., Syst. Nat., ed. 13, 2: 192, 1770.

A. androsaemifolium L. Sp. Pl. of Linnaeus, ed. 4 by Willd.,
    1(2): 1,259, 1797.

Apocinum androsaemi-f. Lestib., Botanogr. Belg., ed. 2, 3:
    83, 1799.

Apocynum muscipulum Moench, Meth. Pl. Hort. Marburg 464,
    1794.

522. *Scirpus maritimus macrostachyus* Michx., Fl. Bor.-Am. 1:
    32, 1803.

S. macrostachyos Lam., Tabl. Encyc. et Méth. 1: 142, 1791.

S. maritimus L. β *macrostachyus* (Michx.) Pers., Syn. Pl.
    1: 68, 1805.

Bolboschoenus macrostachyus (Willd.) Grossh., Fl.
    Caucasus 1: 145, 1928.

S. maritimus L. var. *paludosus* (A. Nels.) Gleason, New
    Britton & Brown Ill. Fl. 1: 276, 1952.

S. robustus Pursh, Fl. Am. Sept. 56, 1814.

    See Britton & Brown, Ill. Fl. N. E. U. S., ed. 2, 1: 333,
    1913.

        Beetle, Am. Jour. Bot. 29: 84, 1942.

        Fernald, Gray's Man. Bot., ed. 8, 272, 1950.

523. *Arctium Lappa* L., Sp. Pl. 816, 1753.

A. Lappa L. ssp. *majus* (Bernh.) J. Arènes, Jard. Bot. État
    Bruxelles, Bul. 20(1): 75–77, 1950.

A. majus Bernh., Syst. Verz. Pfl. Erf. 154, 1800.

Lappa major Gaertn., Fruct. 2: 379, pl. 162, fig. 3, (1791) =
[1802].

L. communis Coss. & Germ. var. β *major* (DC.) Coss. &
Germ., Fl. Env. Paris 389, 1845.

L. vulgaris Hill, Veg. Syst. 4: 28, pl. 25, fig. 1, 1762.

524. *Nototrichium sandwicense* (Gray) Hbd., var. *Forbesii* Sherff,
Bot. Leafl. 2: 2, 1950.

525. *Tiarella cordifolia* L. var. *typica* Lakela, Am. Jour. Bot.
24: 344-351, 1937.

T. cordifolia typica (Lakela) Wherry, Acad. Nat. Sci. Phila.,
Not. Nat. 42: 4, 1940.

526. *Quesnelia* Gaud., Bot. Voy. La Bonite, pl. 54, (1844-1866) =
[1842].

Guesmelia Gaud. ex Walp., Ann. Bot. Syst. 1: 841, 1849.

Lievena Regel, Gartenfl. 29: 289, pl. 1,024, 1880.

527. *Smelowskia ? Californica* Gray, Am. Acad. Arts Sci., Proc.
6: 520, 1866.

528. *Cladium* P. Browne, Civ. Nat. Hist. Jamaica 114, 1756.
Mariscus (Hall.) Zinn, Cat. Hort. Goett. 79, 1757.
See Sprague, Kew Bul. 218, 1934.

529. *Clematis virginiana* L. var. *missouriensis* (Rydb.?) Palmer
& Steyerm., Mo. Bot. Gard., Ann. 22: 542, 1935.

C. Missouriensis Rydb. in Britton, Man. Fl. N. E. U. S.
421, 1901.

C. virginiana L. forma *missouriensis* (Rydb.) Fernald,
Rhodora 39: 309, 1937.

530. *Phlox carolina heterophylla* (Beauvais ex Brand) Wherry,
Bartonia 23: 6-7, 1945.

P. heterophylla Beauvais ex Brand, Engler Pflanzenreich
IV, 250: 55, 1907.

531. *Nymphaea* L., Gen. Pl., ed. 5, 227, 1754; ed. 6, 264, 1764;
Sp. Pl. 510, 1753.

Castalia Salisb. in Koenig & Sims, Ann. Bot. 2: 71-76,
(1806) =[1805, May 1].

Leuconymphaea Ludwig ex Ktze., Rev. Gen. 1: 11, 1891.

Nymphea Raf., Med. Fl. & Bot. U. S. 2: 44-45, 1830.

Nymphozanthus L. C. Rich., Anal. du Fruit 63, 68, 103,
  1808 May; Mus. Paris, Ann. 17: 230, 1811.

Nymphosanthus L. C. Rich., Anal. du Fruit 68, 1808 May;
  Mus. Paris, Ann. 17: 230, 1811.

Nuphar Sm. in Sibth. & Sm., Fl. Graec. Prodr. 1: 361–362,
  1806.

Nenuphar Hayne, Getreue Darstell. u. Beschreib. Arzneik.
  4: pl. 36, 1816.

Blephara Sm., Mem. & Corr. 1: 576, 1832.

Ropalon Raf., New Fl. N. Am. 2: 17, 1836.

Nufar Wallr., Linnaea 14: 582, 1840; (repr. as Erster Beitr.
  Fl. Hercyn.) 212, 1840.

Nymphona Bubani, Fl. Pyr. 3: 260, 1901.

Nelumbo Adans., Fam. Pl. 2: 76, 1763.

Nelumbium Juss., Gen. 68, 1789.

532. *Aplodiscus* DC., Prodr. 5: 350, 1836.

Aplodiscus (DC.) Gray, Am. Acad. Arts Sci., Proc. 8: 638,
  1873.

533. *Nania polymorpha* Gaud. var. *glaberrima* Lévl., Fedde
  Repert. 10: 149, 1911.

Metrosideros collina (J. R. & G. Forst.) Gray ssp. *polymorpha* (Gaud.) Rock var. *glaberrima* (Lévl.) Rock, Terr.
  Hawaii, Board Agric. & For., Div. For., Bot. Bul. 4:
  69–71, pl. 29–30, 1917.

534. *Aristeae* B. & H., Gen. Pl. 3: 684, 1883.

Aristeinae Diels in Engler & Prantl, Nat. Pflanzenfam., ed.
  2, 15a: 480, 1930.

535. *Camellia Thea* Link, Enum. Pl. Hort. Berol. 73, 1822.

Thea sinensis L., Sp. Pl. 515, 1753.

Camellia sinensis (L.) Ktze., Hort. Petrop., Acta 10: 195
  in obs., 1887.

  See Perrier de la Bathie, in Humbert, Fl. Madagascar,
    fam. 134: 11, 1951.

536. *Schiedea salicaria* Hbd., Fl. Haw. Is. 33, 1888.

S. Salicaria Hbd. var. *typica* Sherff, Am. Jour. Bot. 36: 499,
  1949.

537. *Ipomoea acetosaefolia* (Vahl) Vahl ex R. & S., Syst. Veg.
  of Linnaeus, ed. by R. & S., 4: 246, 1819.

Convolvulus acetosaefolius Vahl, Eclog. Am. 1: 18, 1796.

C. littoralis L., Syst. Nat., ed. 10, 924, 1759.

C. stoloniferus Cyrill., Pl. Rar. Neap. 1: 14–17, pl. 5, 1788.

I. littoralis (L.) Boiss., Fl. Orient. 4: 112, 1879.

I. littoralis Bl., Bijdr. Fl. Nederl. Indië 713, 1825.

I. stolonifera (Cyrill.) Gmel., Syst. Nat. of Linnaeus, ed. 13 by Gmel., 2: 345, 1791.

I. carnosa R. Br., Prodr. Fl. Nov. Holl. 485, 1810.

    See van Oostroom, Blumea 3: 540, 1940.

538. *Boerhavia* L., Gen. Pl., ed. 5, 4, 1754; Sp. Pl. 3, 1753.

539. *Anetia* Endl., Gen. Pl. 923, 1839.

Anetium Splitgerber, Nat. Ges., Tiijds. 7: 395, 1840.

Pteridanetium Copel., Gen. Fil. 224, 1947.

    See Morton, Am. Fern Jour. 43(2): 71, 1953.

540. *Corallina barbata* L. Syst. Nat., ed. 10, 1: 806, 1758.

Cymopolia Barbata (L.) Lamx., Hist. Polyp. 293, 1816.

Cymopolia Rosarium Lamx., Hist. Polyp. 294, 1816.

    See Howe in Britton & Millspaugh, Bahama Fl. 605, 1920.

541. *Apiaceae* Lindl., Nat. Syst., ed. 2, 21, 1836.

Ammiaceae Presl, Delic. Prag. 1: 132, 1822.

Umbelliferae Crantz, Class. Umbellif. 41, 1769.

542. *Amida* Nutt., Am. Phil. Soc., Trans. II, 7: 390, 1841.

543. *Przewalskia* Maxim., Acad. Imp. Sci. St.-Pétersb., Bul. 27: 507, 1881.

544. *Cinchona* L., Gen. Pl., ed. 5, 79, 1754; Sp. Pl. 172, 1753.

545. *Eupritchardia* Ktze., Rev. Gen. 3(2): 323, 1898.

Pritchardia Seem. & Wendl. in H. Wendl., Bonplandia 10: 197, 1862; 9: 260, 1861.

Pritchardia Unger in Endl., Gen. Pl., Suppl. 2: 102, 1842.

Pritchardioxylon Drude in Engler & Prantl, Nat. Pflanzenfam., Nachtr. 50, 1897.

546. *Draba Crockeri* Lemmon, Torrey Bot. Club, Bul. 16: 221, 1889.

547. *Acer barbatum* Michx. var. *Longii* (Fern.) Fern. forma *platylobum* (Fern.) Fern., Rhodora 47: 160, 1945.

A. floridanum (Chapm.) Pax var. *Longii* Fern. forma *platylobum* Fern., Rhodora 44: 426–428, pl. 727, 1942.

548. *Pinus tuberculata* sensu Gord., Hort. Soc. London, Jour. 4: 218–220, ill., 1849.

P. tuberculata D. Don, Linn. Soc. Lond., Trans. 17: 442, (1837) =[1836].

P. attenuata Lemmon, Mining & Sci. Press 64: 45, 1892, Jan. 16; Lemmon in Sarg., Gard. & For. 5: 65, 1892, Feb. 10.

549. *Chonemorpha penangensis* Ridley, Straits & Fed. Malay States, Agric. Bul. 10: 146–148, 1911.

550. *Phaseolus acutifolius* Gray, Pl. Wright. 1: 43–44, 1850; Smithsonian Contr. Know. 3(5): 43–44, 1850.

551. *Korthalsella striata* Danser, Jard. Bot. Buitenzorg, Bul. III, 14(2): 124, 1937.

552. *Plectritis californica* (Suksd.) Dyal, Am. Midl. Nat. 42: 495, 1949.

Aligera californica Suksd., Werdenda 1(4): 44, 1927.

A. macrocera (T. & G.) Suksd., Deutsch. Bot. Monatschr. 15(5): 147, 1897.

Plectritis macrocera T. & G., Fl. N. Am. 2: 50, 1841.

553. *Lycopodium venustulum* Gaud. var. *heterophyllum* (Hook.) Hbd. ex Nessel, Die Bärlappgewächse 308, pl. 70, fig. 67, 1939.

L. heterophyllum Hook. & Grev., Icon. Fil. pl. 113, 1831.

L. heterophyllum Grev. & Hook., Bot. Mag. 2: 376, 1831.

554. *Saintpierrea* Germain de Saint Pierre, Journ. des Roses 39, in obs., 1878.

555. *Phylanthera* Noronha, Batav. Gen., Verh., ed. 1, 5(4): 3, 1790.

Phyllanthera Bl., Bijdr. Fl. Nederl. Indië 1,048, (1825) = [1827].

556. *Tillaea* L., Gen. Pl., ed. 5, 62, 1754.

557. *Leveillea* Vaniot, Acad. Intern. Géogr. Bot., Bul. 12: 29, 1903.

558. *Luehea* Willd., Ges. Naturf. Fr., Neue Schr. 3: 410, pl. 5, 1801.

Luhea Willd. ex DC., Prodr. 1: 517, 1824.

559. *Humbertia* Lam., Encyc. Méth. Bot. 2: 356, 1786.

Humbertiella Hochr., Acad. Sci. Paris, Compt. Rendu 182:
1,485, 1926.

Humbertochloa A. Camus & Stapf, Soc. Bot. France, Bul.
81: 467, 1934.

560. *Eragrostis Hosakai* Degener, Fl. Haw., fam. 47: April 16,
1937.

561. *Crepis Froelichiana* DC., Prodr. 7: 165, 1838.

562. *Margyricarpus* Ruiz & Pavon, Fl. Peruv. Prodr. 7, pl. 33,
1794.

563. *Alchemilla vulgaris* L., Sp. Pl. 123, 1753.

A. vulgaris agg., Clapham, Tutin & Warburg, Fl. Brit. Is.
505, 1952.

564. *Geigeria plumosa* Muschl. ampl. Merxm., Bot. Staatssamml.
München, Mitt. 7: 276–277, 1953.

565. *Gynoxys Macfrancisci* Cuatr., Fieldiana Bot. 27(2): 3–4,
1951.

566. *Senecio Alberti-Smithii* Cuatr., Fieldiana Bot. 27(2): 21–22,
1951.

567. *Senecio Fortunatus* Cuatr., Fieldiana Bot. 27(2): 47, 1951.

568. *Heterosporium tshawytschae* Doty & Slater, Am. Midl. Nat.
36: 663–665, 1946.

569. *Canavalia turgida* Grah. in Wall., Cat. (Num. List Pl. E.
Ind.) No. 5,539, 1832.

Lablab microcarpus DC., Prodr. 2: 402, 1825.

C. microcarpa (DC.) Merr., Interp. Rumph. Herb. Amb. 280,
1917.

C. microcarpa (DC.) Piper, Biol. Soc. Wash., Proc. 30:
176, 1917.

570. *Canarium vulgare* Rumph., Herb. Amb. 2: 145–150, pl. 47,
1750; Stickm., Herb. Amb. 9, 1754; Stickm. in L.,
Amoen. Acad. 4: 121, 1759.

C. indicum Stickm. in L., Amoen. Acad. 4: 143, 1759.

C. commune L., Mant. 127, 1767.

571. *Aecidium Hyperici frondosi* Schw., Naturf. Ges.
Leipzig, Schr. 1: 68, 1822.

Uredo hyperici Spreng., Syst. Veg. of Linnaeus, ed. 16 by
Spreng. 4: 572, 1827.

Uromyces triquetrus Cooke, Portland Soc. Nat. Hist., Proc.
1: 184, 1869.

Uromyces Hyperici (Schw.) Curt., Geol. & Nat. Hist. Surv.
N. Carol. Bot. 3: 123, 1867.

Nigredo Hyperici-frondosi (Schw.) Arth., Sci. Congr.
Internat. Bot. Wien, Résult. 344, 1906.

572. *Conomorpha roraimae* Steyerm., Fieldiana Bot. 28(3): 468,
1953.

573. *Trochodendroxylon Beckii* Hergert & Phinney, Torrey Bot.
Club, Bul. 81: 118–122, fig. 1–4, 1954.

574. *Labordia Fagraeoidea* Gaud. var. ε *sessilis* (Gray) Sherff
forma 1 *glabrescens* Sherff, Field Mus. Nat. Hist., Bot.
Ser. 17(6): 481–482, 1939.

575. *Sagittaria Hitchcochii* Gdgr., Soc. Bot. France, Bul. 66:
294, (1919) =[1920].

576. *Avena* Necker, Elem. Bot. 3: 217, 1790.
Avena L., Gen. Pl., ed. 5, 34, 1754.

577. *Litanum* Nieuwl., Am. Midl. Nat. 4: 90, 1915.

578. *Senecio Szyszylowiczii* Hieron., Engler Bot. Jahrb. 36:
508–509, 1905.

579. *Solanum Woahense* Dunal in DC., Prodr. 13(1): 268, 1852.
S. sandwicense H. & A., Bot. Beechey Voy. 42, 1842.
Carex wahuensis C. A. Meyer, Acad. St. Petersb., Mem. 1:
218, pl. 10, 1831.
Chenopodium oahuense (Meyen) Aellen, Ostenia 98–101,
1933.
Lepidium O-Waihiense C. & S., Linnaea 1: 32, 1826.
Eragrostis wahowensis Trin., Acad. St. Petersb., VI, Math.
Phys. Nat. 1: 412, (1830) =[1831].

580. *Erica caffra* L., Sp. Pl. 353, 1753.

581. *Dictyocalyx* Hook. f., Linn. Soc. Lond., Proc. 1: 277, 1849.

582. *Cakile lanceolata* (Willd.) O. E. Schulz, Engler Pflanzenreich IV, 105(2): 26–27, 1923.
C. edentula (Bigel.) Hook., Fl. Bor. Am. 1: 59, (1840) =
[1830].

C. lanceolata (Willd.) O. E. Schulz in Urban, Symb. Antill.
   3(3): 504, 1903.

583. *Pleuropetalum* Hook. f., Linn. Soc. Lond., Proc. 1: 278–
   279, (1849) =[1845].
   Pleuropetalon Bl., Mus. Bot. Lugd.-Bat. 1: 248, 1850.

584. *Prunus serotina* Ehrh. var. *eximia* (Small) Little, Phytologia
   4: 309–310, 1953.
   P. eximia Small, Torreya 1: 146–147, 1901.
   Padus eximia (Small) Small, Fl. S. E. U. S. 573–574, 1,331,
   1903.
   Prunus serotina Ehrh. ssp. *eximia* (Small) McVaugh, Brittonia 7: 302–303, 1951.

585. *Betulinum hanenisiense* Watari, Jap. Jour. Bot. 13: 503–
   506, fig. 1–2, pl. 1A, 1948.
   Betula hanenisiensis (Watari) Watari, Univ. Tokyo, Fac.
   Sci. sect. 3, Bot., Jour. 6(1–3): 107, 1952.

586. *Diplacorchis* Summerh., Kew Bul. 379, 1931.
   Brachycorythoides Summerh., Kew Bul. 379, 1931.
   Eu-Diplacorchis Summerh., Kew Bul. 379, 1931.
   Diplacorchis Schltr., Bot. Centralbl., Beih. 38(2): 127,
   1921.
      See Bullock, Taxon 3: 145, 1954.

587. *Anemone ludoviciana* Nutt., Gen. N. Am. Pl. 2: 20–21,
   1818.
   A. Nuttalliana A. P. DC., Reg. Veg. Syst. Nat. 193, 1818.
   Pulsatilla ludoviciana (Nutt.) Heller, Cat. N. Am. Pl., ed.
   2, 80, 1900.
   A. patens L. var. *Nuttalliana* (A. P. DC.) Gray, Man., ed.
   5, 36, 1867.
   A. patens L. var. *Wolfgangiana* (Bess.) Koch ex Hegi,
   Illustr. Fl. Mitteleur. 3(1): 535, 1912.
   P. patens (L.) Mill. var. *Wolfgangiana* (Bess.) Trautv. &
   Meyer in Midd., Reis. Ausserst. N. & Ost Sibir. 1(2):
   7, 1856.
   P. hirsutissima (Pursh) Britton, New York Acad. Sci., Ann.
   6: 217, 1891.
   P. patens (L.) Mill., Gard. Dict., ed. 8, Pulsatilla No. 4,
   1768.
      See Löve, Svensk. Bot. Tidskr. 48: 219–222, 1954.

588. *Aerva* Forsk., Fl. Aegypt. Arab. 170–171, 1775.

    A. tomentosa Lam., Encyc. Méth. Bot. 1: 46, 1783.

589. *Acacia* ? *tetragonocarpa* Meisn. in Lehm., Pl. Preiss. 1(1): 4, 1844.

    Tetracheilos Meisneri Lehm., Pl. Preiss. 2(2–3): 368, 389, 1848.

590. *Pseudosolidum* McG. ex Lloyd, Mycol. Writ. 7: 1,206, pl. 249, fig. 2,497, 1923.

    Pseudosolidum Lloyd teste Stevenson & Cash, Lloyd Libr. & Mus., Bul. 35 (Mycol. Ser. 8): 22, 1936.

    Hypoxylon solidum Berk. & Curt., Acad. Nat. Sci. Phila., Jour. II, 2: 286, 1854.

    Hypocreopsis solidus Lloyd ex Stevenson & Cash, Lloyd Libr. & Mus., Bul. 35 (Mycol. Ser. 8): 22, fig. 2,497, 1936.

    Rhytisma solidum Schw. ex Stevenson & Cash, Lloyd Libr. & Mus., Bul. (Mycol. Ser. 8): 22, 1936.

591. *Pandanus aruensis* Martelli var. *contractus* Martelli, Engler's Bot. Jahrb. 49(1): 64–65, 1912.

    P. aruensis Martelli, Webbia 4(2): 419–420, pl. 33, fig. 9, 1914.

    P. aruensis Martelli forma *contracta* Martelli, Webbia 4(1): 6, 1913.

592. *Echites puberula* Nutt., Fraser's Cat. 1813; reprinted in Pittonia 2: 117, 1890.

    E. puberula Michx., Fl. Bor.-Am. 1: 120, 1803.

    E. difformis Walt., Fl. Carol. 98, 1788.

    Trachelospermum difforme (Walt.) Gray, Syn. Fl. N. Am. 2(1): 85, 1878.

    Forsteronia difformis (Walt.) A. DC., Prodr. 8: 437–438, 1844.

    Secondatia difformis (Walt.) B. & H., Gen. Pl. 2: 723, 1873.

    Parechtites Thunbergii Gray, Am. Acad. Arts Sci., Mem. 6: 403, 1859.

    See Shinners, Rhodora 57: 290–293, 1955;
        Cronquist *et al.,* Rhodora 58: 23–24, 1956;
        Shinners, Rhodora 58: 281–289, 1956;
        Graustein, Rhodora 58: 20–22, 1956.

593. Torrey, J. & Gray, A., Fl. N. Am. 1: 1838–1840.

594. ×Prunygdalus Moldenke, Phytologia 5: 90, 1954.
     ×*P.* ×*hybrida* Moldenke, Phytologia 5: 90, 1954.

595. *Volvariopsis Earlei* Murr., Mycologia 3: 282, 1911.
     V. Earleae Murr., N. Am. Fl. 10: 142, 1917.

596. *Euphiladelphus* S. Y. Hu, Jour. Arn. Arb. 35: 303, 305, 312, 1954; 36: 52, 1955.

597. *Asplenium Trichomanes ramosum* L., Sp. Pl. 1,083, 1753; ed. 2, 2: 1,541, 1763; ed. 3, 2: 1,541, 1764; Syst. Nat., ed. 13, 2: 690, 1770.
     A. viridi Huds., Fl. Angl. 385–386, 1762.
     A. viride Huds. emend. Sw., Syn. Fil. 80, 1806.

598. *Nardia* S. F. Gray emend. Carrington, Brit. Hepat. 10, 1875.
     Nardius S. F. Gray, Nat. Arr. Brit. Pl. 1: 679, 694, 1821.
     Narda Vell., Fl. Flum. 108, 1825; 3: pl. 24, 1827.
     Nardus L. Gen. Pl., ed. 5, 27, 1754.

CHAPTER 6

600. *Discovium* Raf., Jour. Phys. Chim. Hist. Nat. 89: 96, 1819.
Lesquerella S. Wats., Am. Acad. Arts Sci., Proc. 23: 249–255, 1888.

601. *Equisetum maximum* Lam., Fl. France 1: 7, 1778.
E. Telemateia Ehrh., Hannovers Mag. 287, 1783; Naturk. Wissensch., Beitr. 2: 159, 1788.
 See Milde, Acad. Caes. Leop.-Carol. Germ. Nat. Curios., Nov. Acta 24 (2): 19, 1865.
 Fernald, Rhodora 49: 206, 1947.

602. *Mariscus phleoides* Nees ex Steud., Syn. Pl. Glum. 2: 62, 1855; Nees, Linnaea 9: 286, 1835.
Cyperus phleoides (Nees ex Steud.) Mann, Am. Acad. Arts Sci., Proc. 7: 208, 1867.
Cyperus (Mariscus) phleoides Nees ex Steud., Hbd., Fl. Haw. Is. 469, 1888.

603. *Ochrosia parviflora* Henslow, Ann. Nat. Hist. or Mag. Zool. Bot. Geol. 1: 345–346, 1838.
Cerbera parviflora Forst. f., Flor. Ins. Austral. Prodr. 19, 1786.
O. elliptica Labill., Sert. Austro-Caled. 25, pl. 30, 1824–1825.
O. noumeensis Baill. ex Guillaumin, Mus. Col. Marseille, Ann. 19: 34, 1911.
O. borbonica J. F. Gmel., Syst. Nat. of Linnaeus, ed. 13 by Gmel., 2(1): 439, 1791.
O. maculata Jacq., Icon. Rar. 2: pl. 321, 1786–1793.
Cerbera maculata (Jacq.) Willd., Sp. Pl. of Linnaeus, ed. 4 by Willd., 1(2): 1,223, 1797.
C. parviflora Wallich, Cat. (Num. List Pl. E. Ind.) No. 1,584, 1828.

604. *Acer saccharum* Marsh., Arbustr. Am. 4, 1785.

   A. sacchatum Mill., Gard. Dict., abr. ed. 6, Acer No. 6, 1771.

   A. saccharophorum K. Koch, Hort. Dendrol. 80, 1853.

   A. Treleaseanum Bush, Am. Midl. Nat. 12: 502, 1931.

   See Mackenzie, Rhodora 28: 111, 1926; 28: 233, 1926.

   Sudworth, Rhodora 28: 179, 1926; Bot. Gaz. 100: 312, 1938.

   Sprague, Kew. Bul. 81–82, 1929.

   Bush, Am. Midl. Nat. 15: 784, 1934.

   Rousseau, Inst. Bot. Univ. Montreal, Contr. 35: 1–66, 1940; 42: 17, 1947.

   Gleason, Phytologia 2: 206–209, 1947.

605. *Lithocarpus Rodgerianus* A. Camus, Mus. Hist. Nat. Paris, Bul. II, 4: 913, 1931.

   Pasania Rodgeriana A. Camus, Mus. Hist. Nat. Paris, Bul. II, 3: 690, 1931.

606. *Dryopteris simulata* Davenp., Bot. Gaz. 19: 497, 1894.

   Aspidium simulatum Davenp., Bot. Gaz. 19: 495–496, 1894.

   Nephrodium simulatum Davenp., Bot. Gaz. 19: 497, 1894.

   Lastrea simulata Davenp., Bot. Gaz. 19: 497, 1894.

   Thelypteris simulata (Davenp.) Nieuwl., Am. Midl. Nat. 1: 226, 1910.

607. *Mammea* J. Agardh, Symb. 1: 22, 1841; Linnaea 15: 22, 1841.

   Mammea L., Gen. Pl., ed. 5, 228, 1754.

608. *Amaranthus* L., Gen. Pl., ed. 5, 427, 1754; Sp. Pl. 989–991, 1753.

   Amarantus L., Internat. Code Bot. Nomencl. Stockholm. 44, 1952.

609. *Diodia teres* Walt., Fl. Carol. 87, 1788.

   Spermacoce diodina Michx., Fl. Bor.-Am. 1: 82, 1803.

   See Blake, Rhodora 17: 129, 1915.

   Fernald & Griscom, Rhodora 39: 306, 1937.

610. *Barringtonia* J. R. & G. Forst., Char. Gen. 75–76, pl. 38, 1776.

Butonica Rumph., Herb. Amb. 3: 179–180, pl. 114, 1750.

Agasta Miers, Linn. Soc. Lond., Trans. Bot. II, 1: 59, 1875.

Baranda Llanos, Acad. Cienc. Madrid, Mem. 2: 502, 1859.

Botryoropis Presl, Bohem. Ges., Abh. 6: 580–581, 1851;
    repr. as Epim. Bot. 220, 1849.

Butonica Juss., Gen. Pl. 326, 1789.

Doxomma Miers, Linn. Soc. Lond., Trans. Bot. II, 1: 98–
    107, 1875.

Megadendron Miers, Linn. Soc. Lond., Trans. Bot. II, 1:
    109–111, 1875.

Menichea Sonner., Voy. N. Guin. 133, pl. 92–93, 1776.

Meteorus Lour., Fl. Cochinch. 410, 1790.

Mitraria J. F. Gmel., Syst. Nat. of Linnaeus, ed. 13 by
    Gmel., 799, 1791.

Stravadium Juss., Gen. 326, 1789.

611. *NEO-URBANIA* Fawc. & Rendle, Jour. Bot. Brit. For. 47:
    125, 1909.

612. *Cyathodes imbricata* Stschegleew, Soc. Imp. Nat. Mosc.,
    Bul. 32(1): 10, 1859.

Styphelia Grayana Rock, Ind. Trees Haw. Is. 366, 1913.

S. Douglasii (Gray) F. Muell. in Skottsb., Hort. Gotoburg,
    Acta 2: 255, 1926.

S. Douglasii (Gray) Hochr., Candollea 6: 470, 1936.

613. *Schiedea Gregoriana* Degener, Fl. Haw. 119: 4/9/36.

S. kealiae Caum & Hosaka, Bishop Mus., Occas. Pap.
    11(23): 3–5, 1936, April 10.

614. *Barbosella crassifolia* (Edw.) Schltr. var. *minor* Hoehne,
    Orquidea 11(1): 32, pl. 2, fig. 1, 1948.

615. *Coprosma* J. R. & G. Forst., Char. Gen. 137–138, pl. 69,
    1776.

Euarthronia Nutt. in Gray, Am. Acad. Arts. Sci., Proc. 4:
    49, 1860.

Eurynome DC., Prodr. 4: 475, 1830.

Marquisia A. Rich., Soc. Hist. Nat. Paris, Mém. 5: 192,
    (1834) = [1830].

Pelaphia Banks & Soland. ex A. Cunn., Ann. Nat. Hist. 2:
    206, 1839.

616. *Cestrum Weberbauerei* Francey, Candollea 7: 5–6, 1936.
  See Candollea 7: 509–517, 1938.

617. *Lobelia affinis* Wall., Cat. (Num. List. Pl. E. Ind.), No.
  1,311, 1828; DC., Prodr. 7(2): 360, 1839.
  L. affinis Wall. ex Hook. f. & Thomps., Fl. Brit. Ind. 3:
  424, 1882.
  L. zeylanica L., Sp. Pl. 1,323, 1753.
  L. succulenta Bl., Bijd. Fl. Nederl. Ind. 728, 1825.

618. *Eclipta alba* (L.) Hassk., Pl. Jav. Rarior. 528, 1848.
  Verbesina alba L., Sp. Pl. 902, 1753.
  V. prostrata L., Sp. Pl. 902, 1753.
  Cotula alba (L.) L., Syst. Nat., ed. 12, 2: 564, 1767.
  Eclipta prostrata (L.) L., Mant. Pl. Alt. 286, 1771.
  E. erecta L., Mant. Pl. Alt. 286, 1771.
    See Exell, Cat. Vasc. Pl. S. Tomé 225, 1944.
      Fernald, Rhodora 47: 196–197, 1945.
      Cronquist, Rhodora 47: 398–399, 1945.

619. *Chamaecrista Chamaecrista* (L.) Britton, Torrey Bot. Club,
  Bul. 44: 12, 1917.
  Cassia Chamaecrista L., Sp. Pl. 379, 1753.
  Chamaecrista Pavonis Cass. ex Greene, Pittonia 3: 241,
  1897.

620. *Salacia* L., Mant. Pl. Alt. 2: 159–160, 293, 1771.
  Salacia Pant., Beitr. Kenntn. Foss. Bacill. Ung., ed. 2,
  2: 69–70, 1903.

621. *Malus ioensis* (Wood) Britton in Britton & Brown, Ill. Fl. N.
  States & Can. 2: 235, 1897.
  Pyrus coronaria L. β *Ioensis* Wood, Class-book Bot., rev.
  ed., 334, 1861.
  Pyrus Ioensis (Wood) Bailey, Am. Garden 12: 473–474, fig.
  7–8, 1891.

622. *Dilphinium peregrinum* L., Sp. Pl. 531, 1753.

623. *Herpophyllon* Farlow in De Toni, Syll. Alg. 4(4): 1,713,
  1902.
  Herpophyllum J. Agardh, Analecta Alg. Cont. 2: 62–63,
  1894.

624. *Picria* Lour., Fl. Cochinch. 393, 1790; ed. by Willd., 478, 1793.

> See Merrill, Am. Phil. Soc., Trans. 24 (2): 29, 32, 352, 1935.

625. *Nectria ditissima* Tulasne, Sel. Fung. Carp. 72, pl. 13, fig. 1-4, 1865.

Sphaeria decidua Tode, Fungi Meckl. 2: 31, 1791.

S. coccinea Pers., Icon. & Descr. Fung. 2: 47, pl. 12, fig. 2,a,b,c, 1800; Syn. Fung. 49-50, 1801.

N. coccinea (Pers.) Fr., Summa Veg. Scand. 387, 1849.

Creonectria coccinea (Pers.) Seaver, Mycologia 1: 188-189, 1909.

> See Ashcroft, W. Va. Agric. Exp. Sta., Bul. 261: 27-42, 1934.
>> Petch, Brit. Mycol. Soc. 21: 243-301, 1938.
>> Lohman, Lloydia 6: 98, 1943.

626. *Myroxylon* L. f., Suppl. 34, 1781.

Myroxylon J. R. & G. Forst., Char. Gen. 125, 1776.

Toluifera L., Sp. Pl. 384, 1753.

Xylosma Forst. f., Flor Ins. Austral. Prodr. 72, 1786.

627. *Pandanus Ala-Kai* Martelli, Univ. Calif., Publ. Bot. 17: 174, pl. 24, 1933.

628. *Neyraudia* Hook. f., Fl. Brit. Ind. 7: 305, 1896.

Neraudia Gaud., Bot. Voy. Freyc. Uranie 500, (1826) = [1830].

629. *Phajus Tankervillii* (Banks in L'Her.) Bl., Mus. Bot. Lugd.-Bat. 2: 177, 1856.

Limodorum Tankervilliae Willd., Sp. Pl. of Linnaeus, ed. 4 by Willd., 4: 122, 1805.

L. Tancarvilleae L'Her., Sert. Angl. 28, 1788.

L. Incarvillei Pers., Syn. Pl. 2: 520, 1807.

Bletia Tankervilliae R. Br., Curtis's Bot. Mag. 44: pl. 1,924, 1817.

> See Merrill, Am. Phil. Soc., Trans. n. s. 24 (2): 123, 1935.
> Hawkes, Brittonia 7: 180, 1951.

630. *Trisetum flavescens* Beauv., ssp. I. *T. pratense* (Pers.) Rouy, Fl. France 14: 140, 1913.

631. *Sanicula canadensis* L. var. *genuina* Fern., Rhodora 42:
    467–470, 1940.

    S. canadensis L. var. *typica* H. Wolff, Engler's Pflanzen-
    reich IV, 228: 67, 1913.

632. *Vincentia angustifolia* Gaud., Bot. Voy. Freyc. Uranie 417,
    (1826) = [1829].

    Cladium angustifolium (Gaud.) B. & H., Gen. Pl. 3 (2):
    1,065–1,066, 1883.

    C. angustifolium B. & H. ex Drake, Ill. Fl. Ins. Mar. Pacif.
    334, 1892.

633. *Premna Taitensis* Schauer in DC., Prodr. 11: 638, 1847.

    P. tahitensis DC. emend. F. Br., Bishop Mus., Bul. 130: 3,
    248, 1935.

    Scrophularioides arborea Forst. f., Flor. Ins. Austral. Prodr.
    91, 1786.

    P. arborea Farw., Druggists Circ. 63: 50, 1919.

    P. arborea Roth, Nov. Pl. Sp. 287, 1821.

    Gmelina arborea Roxb. ex Spreng., in Syst. Veg. of Linnaeus,
    ed. 16 by Spreng., 2: 765, 1825.

634. *Weinmannia borneensis* Engler, Nat. Pflanzenfam., ed. 2,
    18A: 255–256, 1930.

    See Heine, Bot. Staatssamml. München, Mitt. 6: 212–213,
    1953.

635. *Elatostemma Pedunculatum* J. R. & G. Forst., Char. Gen.
    105–106, pl. 53, 1776.

    Langeveldia acuminata (Poir.) Gaud., Bot. Voy. Freyc.
    Uranie 494–495, (1826) = [1830].

    Procris acuminata Poir., in Lam. Encyc. Méth Bot. 5: 629,
    1804.

636. *Gonolobus jamaicensis* Rendle, Jour. Bot. Brit. For. 74:
    345, 1936.

    G. rostratus R. Br., Wern. Soc., Mem. 1: 35, 1809.

    G. rostratus sensu Griseb., Flora W. I. 142, 1864.

    G. rostratus sensu Schlecht. in Urb., Symb. Antill. 1: 283,
    1899.

    See Furtado, Gardens' Bul. 12: 331, 1949.

637. *Lantana arubensis* Moldenke, Some New Sp. & Var. Verbenaceae 15–16, n. d.

638. *Elymus condensatus pubens* Piper, Erythea 7: 101, 1899.
E. *condensatus* Presl var. *pubens* Piper ex Hitchc., U. S.
Dept. Agric., Misc. Publ. 200: 253, 843, 1935.
E. *cinereus* (Scribn.) Merr., Torrey Bot. Club, Bul. 29: 467,
1902.

639. *Phaseolus cylindricus* Stickm. in L., Amoen. Acad. 5: 132,
1759.
Vigna cylindrica (L.) Skeels, U. S. Dept. Agric., Bur. Pl.
Ind., Bul. 282: 32, 1913.
Dolichos catjang Burm. f., Fl. Ind. 161, 1768.
Vigna Catjang (Burm. f.) Walp., Linnaea 13: 533, 1839.
See Merrill, Interp. Rumph. Herb. Amb. 284, 1917.
Lawrence, Gent. Herb. 8(1): 44, 1949.

640. *Vernonia Baldwini* Torr., Lyc. New York, Ann. 2: 211, 1828.
V. *interior* Small, Torrey Bot. Club, Bul. 27: 279–280, 1900.
V. *Baldwini interior* Gleason, New York Bot. Gard., Bul. 4:
153, 1906.
V. *interior* Small var. *Baldwini* (Torr.) Mackenzie & Bush,
Man. Fl. Jackson Co. Mo., 190, 1902.
V. *Baldwini* Torr. var. *interior* (Small) Schubert, Rhodora
38: 370, 1936.

641. *Lycopus uniflorus* Michx., Fl. Bor.-Am. 1: 14, 1803.
See Fernald, Rhodora 36: 23–24, 1934.

642. *Rubus alceaefolius* Poir., Lam. Encyc. Méth Bot. 6: 247,
1804.
R. *alceifolius* Poir. emend. Hochr., Candollea 6: 461, 1936.

643. *Andrzeiowskia* Reichb., Icon. Pl. Crit. 1: 15, pl. 13, 1823.
Andreoskia DC., Prodr. 1: 190, 1824.

644. *Vinca rosea* L., Syst. Nat., ed. 10, 2: 944, 1759.
Lochnera rosea (L.) Reichenb., Consp. Regn. Veg. 134,
1828.
Catharanthus roseus (L.) G. Don, Gen. Syst. 4: 95, 1836.
C. *roseus* (L.) G. Don var. *albus* (Sweet) Sweet ex Neal, In
Gard. Hawaii 607, 1948.

645. *Calamagrostis ophitidis* (Th. Howell) Nygren, Hereditas 40: 388, fig. 85–87, 1954.

646. *Athyrium angustipinna* Holttum, Singapore Gardens' Bul. 14: 8, 1953.

647. *Lepidium lasiocarpum* Nutt. ex T. & G., Fl. N. Am. 1: 115, 1838.

648. *Cotinus obovatus* Raf., Autikon Botanikon 82, 1840.
C. americanus Nutt., N. Am. Sylva 3: 1, pl. 81, 1849.
See Little, Okla. Acad. Sci., Proc. 23: 21–23, 1943.

649. *Sphaeria glomus* Berk. & Curt., N. Am. Fungi, No. 957, n. d.; Berk. & Curt. ex Berk., Grevillea 4: 152, 1876.
Ophiolobus ? glomus (Berk. & Curt.) Sacc., Syll. Fung. 2: 347, 1883; ex Underw. & Earle, Alabama Agric. Exp. Sta., Bull. 80: 192, 1897.
Raphidospora glomus (Berk. & Curt.) Cke, Grevillea 18: 16, 1889.

650. *Mikania (§ Thyrsigerae) stereolepis* B. L. Robins., Gray Herb., Contr. 104: 44–45, 1934.

651. *Menthaceae* Piper, U. S. Natl. Herb., Contr. 11: 486, 1906.
Labiatae B. Juss., Hort. Trian., ordo 34, lxiii–lxx, 1759; B. Juss. ex A. L. Juss., Gen. Pl. lxiii–lxx, 1789.
Lamiaceae Lindl, Nat. Syst. Bot. Veg. Kingd. 275, 1836.
Labiaceae Necker, Theod. Palat., Act. 2: 473, 1770.

652. *Cercospora morina* Chupp, Monogr. Fung. Gen. Cercospora 400, (1953) = [1954].
C. moricola Cooke, Grevillea 12: 30, 1883.
C. mori Hara, Sericultural Assoc. Japan, Jour. 27(314): 227 (Arabic 19), 1918.
C. mori Marchal & Steyaert, Soc. Roy. Bot. Belg., Bull. 61: 166, 1929.

653. *Ceramium affine* Setch. & Gardn. var. *originale* Dawson, Farlowia 4: 133, 1950.

654. *Dicarphus rubens* Raf., Med. Repos. II, 3: 423, 1806; II, 5: 355, 1808; Jour. Bot. (Paris) 2: 176, 1809; Specch. Sci. 1: 194, 1814; Anal. Nat. Tabl. Univ. 211, 1815; repr. in Lloyd, Mycol. Notes 1(13) 129, 1903.

See Gerard, Torrey Bot. Club, Bul. 12: 37, 1885;
Merrill, Farlowia 1: 257, 1943.

655. *Spegazzinia* Backeb., Kakteenfreund, 2(10): 117, 1933.

656. *Aërides* Lour., Fl. Cochinch. 525, 1790.

657. *Jarava* Ruiz & Pavon, Fl. Peruv. Prodr. 2, pl. 1, 1794.
Stipa L., Gen. Pl., ed. 5, 14, 1754; Sp. Pl. 78, 1753.

658. *Fevillea* L., Gen. Pl., ed. 5, 443, 1754; Sp. Pl. 1,013, 1753.

659. *Aconitum kunasilense* Nakai, Natl. Sci. Mus. (Tokyo), Bul.
32: 21, 1953.

660. *Phleum pratense* L. ssp. *vulgare* (Čel.) Asch. & Graebn.
emend. Hyl., Bot. Notis. 357, 1953.
P. pratense L., ssp. A *P. vulgare* (Čel.) Aschers. &
Graebn., Syn. Mitteleur. Fl. 2(7): 141–142, 1899.
P. pratense L. *a vulgare* Čelakovsky, Prodr. Fl. Böhm. 38,
1867.
P. pratense L. s. str. Sterner ap. Lindman, Svensk Fanero-
gamfl., ed. 2, 74, 1926.

661. *Pteronevron* Fée, Gen. Fil, in Mém. Fam. Foug. 5: 204,
320, pl. 25, B, fig. 1, (1850–1852) = [1852].
See Pichi-Sermolli, Webbia 9: 361–362, 1953.
Rickett, Taxon 4: 185–188, 1955.

662. *Senecio Danielis* Cuatr., Fieldiana Bot. 27(2): 31, 1951.

663. *Avena fatua* L. ampl. Hausskn. ssp. *eufatua* Hyl., Bot.
Notis 355, 1953.
A. fatua L. ssp. *fatua* Thell., Naturf. Ges. Zürich, Viertel-
jahrsschr. 56: 319-320, 1911.
A. fatua L., Sp. Pl. 80, 1753.

664. *Solanum incompletum* Dunal in DC., Prodr. 13(1): 311, 1852.

665. *Artemisia columbiensis* Nutt., Gen. N. Am. Pl. 2: 142,
1818.
A. cana Pursh, Fl. Am. Sept. 2: 521, 1814.
See Ward, G. H., Dudley Herb., Contr. 4(6): 156, 188,
1953.

666. *Cuscuta africana* Willd., Sp. Pl. of Linnaeus, ed. 4 by
Willd., 1(2): 703, 1797.

Schrebera Schinoides L., Sp. Pl., ed. 3, 1,662, 1764.
Schinus myricoides L., Sp. Pl. 388, 1753.

667. *Gouldia terminalis* (H. & A.) Hbd. var. *kaala* Fosb. forma *eukaala* Fosb., Bishop Mus., Bul. 147: 49, 1937.

668. *Gouldia terminalis* (H. & A.) Hbd. var. *Hosakai* Fosb., Bishop Mus., Bul. 147: 38, 1937.

669. *Acanthonitschkea* Speg., Buenos Aires Mus. Nac., Ann. III, 10: 116, 1908.

670. *Macraea* Lindl., Quart. Jour. Sci. Lit. & Art 25: 104, 1828.
Macraea Hook. f., Linn. Soc. Lond., Proc. 1: 278, 1849.
Macraea Wight, Icon. 5: 27, 1852.

671. *Jeffreya Shastensis* Oreg. Comm. [Rept. 8]: third Page, [1853].

672. *Elaphoglossum reticulatum* Gaud., Bot. Voy. La Bonite, Atlas pl. 79, fig. 1–4, 1844.

673. *Crucita hispanica* L., Sp. Pl., ed. 2, 179, 1762.
Cruzita hispanica L., Syst. Nat., ed. 12, 129, 1767.

674. *Rumex Britannica* L., Sp. Pl. 334, 1753.

675. *Desmocephalum* Hook. f., Linn. Soc. Lond., Proc. 1: 277–278, 1849.

676. *Bostrychia harveyi* Mont. ecad *distans* (Harv.) De Berg, Farlowia 3 (4): 500–502, fig. 2, 1949.
B. distans ? Harv. in Hook. f., (Fl. Tasmania), Bot. Antarctic Voy. Erebus & Terror 5: 299, 1860.
B. distans Harv. in Hook. f., (Fl. N. Zeal. 2:), Bot. Antarctic Voy. Erebus & Terror 4: 226, 1855.
See Silva, Univ. Calif., Publ. Bot. 25: 269, 1952.

677. *Ceanothus Americanus* (L.) T. & G., Fl. N. Am. 1: 264, (1838–1840) = [1838].

678. *Quercinum anataiense* Watari, Jap. Jour. Bot. 11: 399–403, fig. 4–5, photo 2, D-G, 1941.
Quercus anataiensis (Watari) Watari, Univ. Tokyo, Fac. Sci., Jour., Ser. III, Bot. 6 (1–3): 107, 1952.

679. *Pentaglossum linifolium* Forsk., Fl. Aegypt. Arab. 11, 1775.

680. *Secula viscidula* (Michx.) Small, Fl. Miami 90, 200, 1913.
Aeschynomene viscidula Michx. Fl. Bor.-Am. 2: 74-75,
1803.

681. *Kyrtandra* Gmel., Syst. Nat. of L., ed. 13 by Gmel., 2: 37,
1791.
Cyrtandra Juss., Gen. Pl. 121, 1789.
Kyrtandra aristata Blanco, Fl. Filip. 18, 1837.

682. *Roxburghia* Roxb., Pl. Coast Corom. 1: 29, pl. 32, 1795.
Roxburghia Koenig ex Carey, Roxb., Fl. Ind., ed. Carey,
1: 168, 1820.
Roxburghia Koenig ex Carey, Roxb., Fl. Ind., ed. Carey,
3: 34, 1832.
See Rafinesque's assertion that Roxburgh names *Roxburghia* for himself, Raf., Fl. Tellur. 1: 17,
(1836) =[1837]; 2(1): 96, (1836) =[1837].

683. *Boehmeria* Jacq., Enum. Pl. Carib. 9, 31, 1760.

684. *Rhynchospora spicaeformis* Hbd., Fl. Haw. Is. 477, 1888.
R. spiciformis Hbd. emend. Skottsb., Hort. Gotob., Acta
15: 321, 1944.

685. *Chaerophyllum Tainturieri* Hook. var. *floridanum* C. & R.,
U. S. Natl. Herb., Contr. 7: 60, 1900.

686. *Clermontia Kakeana* Meyen, Reise um die Erde 2: 358,
1834.

687. *Cambogia G. Gutta* L., Gen. Pl., ed. 5, addenda, 1754.
C. Gutta L., Sp. Pl., ed. 2, 728, 1762; ed. 3, 728, 1764.
Garcinia cambogia Desr. in Lam., Encyc. Méth. Bot. 3:
701, (1789) =[1791].

688. *Hippocratea Urceolus* Tul. S. sp. *xerophila* H. Perr., Mus.
Col. Marseille, Ann. V, 10: 27, 1942.

CHAPTER 7

700. *Santolina ChamaeCyparissus* L., Sp. Pl. 842, 1753.
S. Chamae Cyparissus L., Sp. Pl., ed. 3, 2: 1,179, 1764.
Santolina Chamaecyparissus L. ex Hegi, Fl. Mitteleur.
6(2): 672, 1929.
S. chamaecyparissus L. ex Neal, In Gardens of Hawaii 749,
1949.

701. *Lycopodium ecuadoricum* Herter, Engler's Bot. Jahrb. 34:
48, 1909.
Urostachys Rolandii-principes Herter ex Nessel, Die
Bärlappgewächse 117, 1939.
U. rolandi-principis Herter ex Nessel emend. Herter, Index
Lycop. 79, 1949.

702. *Limnanthes gracilis* Howell, Fl. N. W. Am. 1: 108, 1897.
L. gracilis Howell var. *gracilis*, Mason, Univ. Calif., Publ.
Bot. 25(6): 487, 1952.

703. *Pteridium* Gleditsch in Scop., Fl. Carn. 169, 1760.
Pteridium (Kuetz.) J. Agardh, Sp. Gen. Ord. Alg. 3(3): 218,
1898; 4(1): 710–716, 1897.

704. *Ficus benghalensis* L., Sp. Pl. 1,059, 1753; ed. 3, 1,514,
1864.
F. bengalensis L. ex Barrett, Torrey Bot. Club, Bul. 72:
394, 1945.

705. *Agatea* Gray, U. S. Expl. Exped. Bot. 15: 89–92, 1854.
agataea Cass., Soc. Philom. Paris, Bul. Sci. 175, 1815.
Agati Adans., Fam. Pl. 2: 326, 1763.
Agation Brongn., Soc. Bot. France, Bul. 8: 79, 1861.
Agathis Salisb., Linn. Soc. Lond., Trans. 8: 311–312, pl.
15, 1807.
Agasta Miers, Linn. Soc. Lond. Bot., Trans. II, 1: 59,
1875.

706. *Astragalus dispermus dispermus* James, Dudley Herb.,
Contr. 4(4): 67–68, 1951.
A. dispermus Gray, Am. Acad. Arts Sci., Proc. 13: 365,
1878.

707. *Taxodium Washingtonium* Winslow, Calif. Farmer (San Fran-
cisco newspaper) 2: 58, Aug. 24, 1854.
See St. John & Krauss, Pacif. Sci. 8: 341–358, 1954.
Rousseau, Taxon 4: 40–42, 1955.

708. *Stewartia montana, fol. ovatis acuminatis*, W. Bartr., Travels N. Car. Florida 334, 1791.
See Merrill, Bartonia 23: 12, 1945.

709. *Ficus Beniamina* L., Mant. 129, 1767.
F. benjamina L., Syst. Nat., ed. 13, 2: 681, 1770.
F. benjamina L. var. *nuda* (Miq.) Barrett, Am. Midl. Nat.
45: 127–128, 1951.
Urostigma nudum Miq., Hooker's Lond. Jour. Bot. 6: 584,
1847.
U. benjamineum var. *nuda* (Miq.) Miq., Pl. Jungh. 1: 50,
1853.
Ficus nuda (Miq.) Miq., Mus. Bot. Lugd. Bat., Ann. 3: 267,
1867.

710. *Boldu* Adans., Fam. Pl. 2: 446, 1763.
Boldus Adans. emend. Schult. f. in R. & S., Syst. Veg. of
Linnaeus, ed. nova by R. & S., 7: p. X, 56, 1829.

711. *Lobelia Gaudichaudii* DC., Prodr. 7: 384, 1838.
L. Gaudichaudii DC. var. *coccinea* Rock, Torrey Bot. Club,
Bul. 44: 238, pl. 15, 56, 57, 1917.
L. Gaudichaudii DC. var. *typica* St. John & Hosaka, Bishop
Mus., Occas. Pap. 14(8): 118–120, 1938.

712. *Cercocarpus betuloides* Nutt. ex T. & G., Fl. N. Am. 1:
427, 1840.
C. alnifolius Rydb., N. Am. Fl. 22: 421, 1913.
C. betulaefolius Nutt. var. *Blancheae* Schneid., Deut.
Dendrol. Gesell., Mitt. 14: 127, 1905.
C. betuloides Nutt. var. *alnifolius* (Rydb.) Dunkle, S. Calif.
Acad. Sci., Bul. 39: 2, 1940.
C. montanus Raf. var. *blanchae* (Schneid.) F. L. Martin,
Brittonia 7: 103, 1950.

C. betuloides Nutt. var. *blanchae* (Schneid.) Little,
Phytologia 4: 308, 1953.

C. montanus Raf. var. *glaber* (S. Wats.) F. L. Martin, Brittonia 7: 101-102, 1950.

713. *Paeonia lactiflora* Pall., Reise Russ. Reiche 3: 286, 1776.

P. albiflora Pall., Fl. Ross. 1(2): 92, 1788.

Poeonia albiflora Pall., Fl. Ross. 1(2): pl. 84, 1788.

Paeonia edulis Hook., Parad. Lond. pl. 78, (1805) = [1807].

P. edulis Reevesiana Paxt., Mag. Bot. 1: 197, 1834.

P. Reevesiana Paxt. in Loud., Hort. Brit., ed. nov. suppl. 601, 1850.

See Lynch, Roy. Hort. Soc., Jour. 12: 428-445, 1890.
Huth, Engler Bot. Jahrb. 14: 258-276, 1891.
Finet & Gagnepain, Soc. Bot. France, Bul. 51: 523-527, 1904.
Komarov, Fl. C.C.C.R. 7: 25-26, 1937.
Stebbins, Univ. Calif., Publ. Bot. 19: 252, 1939.

714. *Adelia* P. Browne, Civ. Nat. Hist. Jamaica 361, pl. 36, fig. 3, 1756.

Adelia L., Syst. Nat., ed. 10, 2: 1,298, 1759.

Borya Labill., Nov. Holl. Pl. Spec. 1: 81, pl. 107, 1804.

Borya Willd., Sp. Pl. of Linnaeus, ed. 4 by Willd., 4(2): 711, 1806.

Forestiera Poir. in Lam. Encyc. Méth. Bot. Suppl. 1: 132, 1810; 2: 664, 1811.

715. *Anelsonia* Macbr. & Pays., Bot. Gaz. 64: 81, 1917.

716. *Melobesia membranacea* (Esper.) Lamx., Soc. Philom. Paris, Nouv. Bul. Sci. 3(63): no. 29, 1812.

717. *Raillardia rocki* Sherff, Bot. Gaz. 95: 79, 1933.

Railliardia Rockii Sherff, Bishop Mus., Bul. 135: 130-131, 1935.

Dubautia Rockii (Sherff) Keck, Bishop Mus., Occas. Pap. 11(19): 28, 1936.

See St. John, Pacif. Sci. 4: 342, 1950.

718. *Senecio mortuosus* Standl. ex Morton, Phytologia 4(4): 262-263, 1953.

719. *Cystopteris fragilis* (L.) Bernh. forma *simulans* Weatherby, Rhodora 37: 376, 1935.

720. *Didymosphaeria Equiseti-hiemalis* Larsen & Munk, Dansk
Bot. Arkiv 14: 17–18, fig. 6, 1952.

721. *Cydonia Cydonia* (L.) Pers., Syn. Pl. 2: 40, 1807.
Pyrus Cydonia L., Sp. Pl. 480, 1753.
Cydonia Oblonga Mill., Gard. Dict., ed. 8, Cydonia No. 1,
1768.
C. vulgaris Pers., Syn. Pl. 2: 40 corrigenda, 1807.

722. *Campanula caulibus diffusis, foliis subovatis integerrimis*
L., Sp. Pl. 169, 1753.

723. *Castalia Leibergi* Morong, Bot. Gaz. 13: 124, 1888.
Nymphaea Leibergi Morong, Bot. Gaz. 13: 124, 1888.

724. *Trymalium ramosissimum* Audas, Austral. Bushland 283,
1950.

725. *Naegelia* Regel, Flora 31: 249, 1848.
Nägelia Zoll. & Mor., Syst. Verz. Zoll. 20, 1845–1846.

726. *Eupatorium verticillatum* Lam., Encyc. Méth. Bot. 2: 405,
1786.
E. purpureum L., Sp. Pl. 838, 1753.
See Farwell, Mich. Acad. Sci., Rept. 20: 192, 1918.
Wiegand, Rhodora 22: 57–70, 1920.
Mackenzie, Rhodora 22: 157–165, 1920; 29: 6–9,
1927.
Wiegand & Weatherby, Rhodora 39: 297–306, 1937.
Jennings, Castanea 7: 43–48, 1942.
Fernald, Rhodora 47: 193, 1945.

727. *Solanum vestitum* Nutt. ex Seem., Fl. Vit. 174, 1866.
S. vestitum Benth. in Maund, Botanist 4: text and pl. 192,
1839.
S. Nelsoni Dunal β var. *thomasiaefolium* Seem., Jour. Bot.
Brit. For. 1: 209, 1863.

728. *Pandorea* J. Agardh in de Toni, Syll. Algar. 6(5): 752, 1924.
Pandorea (Endl.) Spach, Hist. Nat. Vég. Phan. 9: 136,
1840.
Pandorea Endl., Gen. Pl. 711, 1836–1840.

729. *Anthochloa* Nees in Meyen, Reise um Erde 2: 14, 1835.
Stapfia Davy, Erythea 6: 109–111, pl. 3, 1898.
Stapfia Chodat, Herb. Boissier, Bul. 5: 939–947, pl. 23,
1897.

Neostapfia Davy, Erythea 7: 43, 1899.

Davyella Hack., Oesterr. Bot. Zeitschr. 49: 133–134, 1899.

730. *Lobelia macrostachys* H. & A., Bot. Beechey Voy. 88, 1832.

Trematocarpus macrostachys (H. & A.) Zahlbr., K. K. Naturhist. Hofmus. Wien, Ann. 6(3–4): 430–432, fig. 1–5, 1891.

Trematocarpus Kuetz., Phyc. Gen. 410, pl. 51, fig. 1, 1843.

Trematolobelia macrostachys (H. & A.) Zahlbr. in Rock, Coll. Hawaii Publ., Bul. 2: 45, pl. 11–12, 1913.

Trematolobelia sandwicensis Degener, Fl. Haw. 339: 10/15/'34.

731. *Aleurites triloba* J. R. & G. Forst., Char. Gen. Pl. 111–112, pl. 56, 1776.

Camirium [Rumph.] Gaertn., Fruct. 2: 194–196, pl. 125, 1791.

Dryandra Thunb., Fl. Jap. 13, pl. 27, 1784.

Elaeococca A. Juss., Euphorb. Gen. Tent. 38, pl. 11, 1824.

Telopea Soland. ex Baill., Gen. Euphorb. 345, 1858.

732. *Debregeasia* Gaud., Bot. Voy. La Bonite, pl. 90, (1844–1866) =[1844].

Leucocnide Miq., Pl. Jungh. 1: 36–37, 1851.

Morocarpus Sieb. & Zucc., Math. Phys. Acad. Muench., Abhandl. 4(3): 218, 1846.

733. *Panicum spinescens* R. Br., Prodr. Fl. Nov. Holl. 193, 1810.

Chamaeraphis spinescens (R. Br.) Poir. in Lam., Encyc. Méth. Bot. Suppl. 2: 189, 1811.

Pseudoraphis spinescens (R. Br.) Vickery, Roy. Soc. Queensland, Proc. 62(7): 69–71, 1952.

Panicum asperum Koenig, Naturforscher 23: 209, 1788.

Chamaeraphis aspera (Koen.) Nees in Wall., Cat. (Num. List Pl. E. Ind.), No. 8,679, 1849.

Pseudoraphis aspera (Koen.) Pilger, Bot. Gard. Berlin, Notizbl. 10: 210, 1928.

Panicum abortivum R. Br., Prodr. Fl. Nov. Holl. 193, 1810.

Chamaeraphis abortiva (R. Br.) Poir. in Lam. Encyc. Méth. Bot. Suppl. 2: 184, 1811.

Orthopogon abortivus (R. Br.) Spreng., Syst. Veg. of Linnaeus, ed. 16 by Spreng., 1: 306, 1825.

734. *Aster Fendleri* Gray, Am. Acad. Arts Sci., Mem. II, 4: 66, 1849.

Aster Nuttallii T. & G. var. *Fendleri* (Gray) Gray, Pacif. R. R. Rept. 4(5): 97, 1856.

735. *Ixora nigritans* R. Br. ex Wall., Cat. (Num. List Pl. E. Ind.) No. 6,154, 1828.

I. nigritans Wight ex Wall., Cat. (Num. List Pl. E. Ind.) No. 1,335, 1833.

I. nigritans R. Br. in Wight & Arn., Prodr. Fl. Penin. Ind. Orient. 1: 428, 1834.

736. *Glochidion* J. R. & G. Forst., Char. Gen. 113–114, pl. 57, 1776.

Bradleia Cav., Icon. Descr. Pl. Hispan. 4: 48, pl. 371, 1797.

Bradleja Banks ex Gaertn., Fruct. 2: 127, pl. 109, 1791.

Glochidionopsis Bl., Bijdr. Fl. Nederl. Indië 2: 588, 1825.

Glochisandra Wight, Icon. Pl. Ind. Orient. 5(2): 28, pl. 1,905, 1852.

Gynoon A. Juss., Mus. Hist. Nat. Paris, Mém. 10: 335, 1823.

Lobocarpus Wight & Arn., Prodr. Fl. Penins. Ind. Orient. 7, 1834.

737. *Mentha bracteolata* Opiz, Seznam 65, 1852.

M. bracteolata Opiz ex Déséglise, Soc. Etud. Sci. Angers, Bul. 1881–1882: 210, 1882.

738. *Variegatae* Krukoff, Jour. Arn. Arb. 20: 226, 1939.

739. *Pavia* [Boerh.] Mill., Gard. Dict., ed. 8, Pavia, *1768*. See Rickett, Taxon 4: 185–188, 1955.

740. *Serrafalcus Lloydianus* Gren. & Godr., Fl. France 3: 591, 1855.

741. *Macaranga quadriglandulosa* Warb. var. *variabilis* Perry, Jour. Arn. Arb. 34: 239, 1953.

742. *Urostachys sulcinervius* (Spring) Hert. var. *kanaiensis* Hbd. ex Nessel, Die Bärlappgewächse 54, pl. 7, fig. 7, 1939.

743. *Aëtia* Adans., Fam. Pl. 2: 84, 1763.

744. *Cucurbita Citrullus* L., Sp. Pl. 1,010–1,011, 1753.
Citrullus Forsk., Fl. Aegypt. Arab. 167, 1775.
Anguria Mill., Gard. Dict., abr. ed. 4, 1: [83], 1754.
Cococynthis Ludwig, Inst. Regn. Veg., ed. 2, 139, 1757.
Citrullus vulgaris Schrad. in Ecklon & Zeyher, Enum. Pl.
    Afr. Austr. Extratrop. 279, 1836.
  See Hara, Bot. Mag. [Tokyo] 61: 716, 1948; Taxon 2:
      134–135, 1953;
      Fosberg, Taxon 2: 99–101, 1953; 3: 2, 1954; 5: 15,
        1956;
      Meeuse, Taxon 4: 198, 1955.

745. *Quercus rubra* L., Sp. Pl. 996, 1753.
Q. borealis Michx. f., Hist. Arbres Forest. Am. Sept., Engl.
    ed. as N. Am. Sylva 1: 119–121, pl. 26, 1817.
Q. borealis Michx. f. var. *maxima* (Marsh.) Sarg., Rhodora
    18: 48, 1916.
Q. rubra L. var. *borealis* (Michx. f.) House, New York State
    Mus., Bul. 243–244: 60, 1923.
  See Sargent, Rhodora 18: 47, 1916.
    Mackenzie, Rhodora 30: 235, 1928.
    Svenson, Rhodora 41: 522, 1939.
    Palmer, Am. Midl. Nat. 27: 732, 1942.

746. *Euphorbia maculata* L., Sp. Pl. 455, 1753.
E. supina Raf., Am. Monthly Mag. Crit. Rev. 2: 119, 1817.
Xamesike supina (Raf.) Raf., Aut. Bot. 97, (1815–1840) =
    1840.
  See Wheeler, Gray Herb., Contr. 127: 76, 1939; Rhodora
      48: 197–200, 1946.
    Svenson, Rhodora 47: 273–302, 363–388, 1945.
    Croizat, Torrey Bot. Club, Bul. 74: 153–155, 1947.
    Fosberg, Torrey Bot. Club, Bul. 74: 332–333, 1947;
      Rhodora 55: 241–243, 1953.

747. *Thelephora laevis* Pers. ex Fries, Syst. Mycol. 1: 451,
    1821.
Peniophora laevis (Pers. ex Fries) Burt, Mo. Bot. Gard.,
    Ann. 12: 257, (1925) = [1926].
P. affinis Burt, Mo. Bot. Gard., Ann. 12: 266, (1925) =
    [1926].

See Burt, Mo. Bot. Gard., Ann. 13: 280, (1925) = [1926].
Rogers & Jackson, Farlowia 1: 318, 1943.

748. *Mercurialis perennis* L., Sp. Pl. 1,035, 1753.
M. montana testiculata Bauh., Pinax 122, 1671.
M. montana spicata Bauh., Pinax 122, 1671.

749. *Heterobasidion* Bref., Unters. Ges. Myk. 8: 154, (1889) =
[Nov. 1888].
Heterobasidium Massee, Linn. Soc. Lond. Bot., Jour. 25:
127–128, 1889.

750. *Musaenda fr frondoso* L., Sp. Pl. 177, 1753.
M. frondosa L. ex Stickm., Herb. Amboin. 17, 1754; Linnaeus, Amoen. Acad. 4: 127, 1760.

751. *Gynoxis sancti-antonii* Cuatr., Fieldiana Bot. 27(1): 9,
1950.

752. *Ficus vilamilii* (Merr.) Sata, Monogr. Stud. Ficus, Taihoku
Imp. Univ., Fac. Agric., Inst. Hort. & Econ. Bot.,
Contr. 32(1): 183, 1944.

753. *Philacra auriculata* Dwyer, Brittonia 5: 126, 1944.

754. *Coreopsis tinctoria* Nutt., Acad. Nat. Sci. Phila., Jour. 2:
114–115, 1821.
C. tinctoria Nutt. forma *atropurpurea* (Hook.) Fern., Rhodora
44: 477, 1942.
C. tinctoria Nutt. var. *atropurpurea* Hook. forma *tinctoria*
Sherff, Brittonia 6: 341, 1948.
Calliopsis tinctoria (Nutt.) Hook. var. *atropurpurea* Hook.,
Curtis's Bot. Mag. 63: pl. 3,511, 1836.

755. *Cephalanthus occidentalis* L. forma *lanceolatus* Fern.,
Rhodora 49: 181, 1947.

756. *Acinaria* Raf., Jour. Phys. Chim. Hist. Nat. 89: 107, 1819;
Isis von Oken 1820: 1: Lit. Anz. 243, 1820.
Nitella Ag., Syst. Alg. xxvii, 1824; emend. A. Braun,
Hooker's Jour. Bot. & Kew Miscell. 1: 193–195, 1849.
See Wood, Torrey Bot. Club, Bul. 75: 283–284, 1948.

757. *Peridinium claudicanoides* Graham, Carnegie Inst. Wash.,
Publ. 542: 24, fig. 29, 1942.

758. *Labordia Cyrtandrae* (Baill.) Skottsb., Hort. Gotoburg, Acta
10: 156, 1936.

L. Cyrtandrae (Baill.) St. John, Bishop Mus., Occas. Pap.
   12(8): 5, 1936.
Geniostoma Cyrtandrae Baill., Soc. Linn. Paris, Bul. 1:
   239, 1880.

759. *Rhynchospora glauca* Vahl var. *chinensis* (Boeck.) C. B.
   Clarke forma *spicaeformis* (Hbd.) Kükenth. ex Skottsb.,
   Hort. Gotoburg, Acta 2: 213, 1926.
   R. glauca Vahl ssp. *lavarum* (Gaud.) Kükenth. var. *spicae-
   formis* (Hbd.) Kükenth., Engler Bot. Jahrb. 75: 150,
   1950.
   R. spicaeformis Hbd., Fl. Haw. Is. 477, 1888.

760. *Styphelia Banksii* (Gaud.) F. Muell., Fragm. Phytogr.
   Austral. 6: 57, 1867.
   Cyathodes Banksii Gaud., Bot. Voy. Freyc. Uranie 98,
   (1826) =[1827].

761. *Salix alexensis* Cov. ex Briggs, Rhodora 55: 249, 1953.
   S. alaxensis (Anderss.) Cov., Wash. Acad. Sci., Proc. 2:
   280, 1900.
   S. speciosa H. & A. β *Alaxensis* Anderss. in A. DC., Prodr.
   16(2): 275, 1868.

762. *Clermontia montis-Loa* Rock, Coll. Hawaii, Bul. 2: 40, pl.
   9, 1913.
   See Rock, Bishop Mus., Mem. 7(2): 334, 1919.

763. *Danthonia spicata pinetorum* Piper, Erythea 7: 104, 1899.
   Meranthrepta pinetorum Piper, U. S. Natl. Herb., Contr. 11:
   122, 1906.
   M. thermale (Scribn.) Heller ex Fedde & Schust., Just's Bot.
   Jahresber. 37(2): 128, 1911.
   D. thermale Scribn., U. S. Dept. Agric., Div. Agrostol.,
   Circ. 30: 5, 1901.

764. *Phyllostegia parviflora* (Gaud.) Benth., Linnaea 6: 79,
   1831.
   P. parviflora (Gaud.) Benth. var. *Gaudichaudii* Gray, Am.
   Acad. Arts Sci., Proc. 5: 344, 1861.
   Prasium parviflorum Gaud., Bot. Voy. Freyc. Uranie 453,
   (1826) =[1829]; Atlas pl. 65, fig. 1, 1826.

765. *Railliardia scabra* DC., Prodr. 6: 441, 1837.
   R. scabra DC. var. *hispidula* Gray, Am. Acad. Arts. Sci.,
   Proc. 5: 133, 1861.

Dubautia scabra (DC.) Keck, Bishop Mus., Occas. Pap.
11(19): 26, 1936.
See Sherff, Brittonia 6: 338, 1948.
St. John, Pacif. Sci. 4: 342, 1950.

766. *Betula caerulea-grandis* Blanchard, Betula 1(1): one page
unnumbered, 1904.

767. *Carex chikungana* Bailey, Gent. Herb. 1: 13, 1920.
Saussurea oxydonta Hultén, Kungl. Svenska
Vetenskapsakad., Handl. III, 8(2): 207, 1930.

768. *Cyrtandra velutina* Nad., Jour. Bot. (ed. Morot) 13: 4, 1899.

769. *Eugenia hawaiiensis* Degener, Fl. Haw. 273: 7/15/'32.

770. *Lupinus alpicola* Henders. in Piper, U. S. Natl. Herb.,
Contr. 11: 355–356, 1906.

771. *Nemacladus pinnatifidus* Greene, Calif. Acad. Sci., Bul. 1:
197, 1885.
N. ramosissimus Nutt. var. *pinnatifidus* (Greene) Gray,
Synopt. Fl. N. Am. 2(1): Suppl. 393, 1886.

772. *Bidens waianensis* Sherff, Bot. Gaz. 70: 104, 1920.
B. waianaeensis Sherff emend. Skottsb., Hort. Gotoburg.,
Acta 15: 508, 1944.

773. *Macaranga salomonensis* Perry, Jour. Arn. Arb. 34: 210,
1953.

774. *Rosa acicularis* Lindl. var. *lacorum* Erlanson, Mich. Acad.
Sci. Arts Letters, Pap. 5(1925): 86, 1926.
R. acicularis Lindl. var. *lacuum* Erlanson emend. Butters &
Abbe, Rhodora 55: 169, 1953.

775. *Lypochaeto australis* Less. var. *denticulata* Wawra, Flora
56: 77, 1873.
Lipochaeta lobata (Gaud.) DC. var. γ *denticulata* (Wawra)
Sherff, Bot. Gaz. 95: 92, 1933.
See Rickett, Taxon 4: 185–188, 1955.

776. *Aporosa* Bl., Bijdr. Fl. Nederl. Ind. 12: 514, 1825.
Aporusa Bl. emend. Bl. in Bl. & Fish., Fl. Jav. 1: vi, 1828.
See Croizat, Bot. Gard. Buitenzorg, Bul. III, 17(2): 217,
1942.

777. *Odontoglossum auropurpureum* Reichb. f., Linnaea 22: 848,
1849.

O. aureo-purpureum Reichb. f. emend. Reichb. f., Gard.
  Chron. n. s. 3: 492, 1875.
  See Schweinfurth, Harvard Univ. Bot. Mus., Leafl. 14(3):
    63, 1949.

778. *Lycopodium complanatum* L. Unterart *L. chamaecyparissus*
  A. Braun forma Monstr.-*triceps* Milde, Acad. Caes.
  Leop.-Carol., Nova Acta 26(2): 407, 1858.
  See Nessel, Die Bärlappgewächse 329, 1939.

779. *Padina Howeana* Børg., Dansk Bot. Arkiv 2(1): 442, 1920.
  Dictyota variegata Lamx., Mus. Hist. Nat. Paris, Ann. 20:
    272, 1813; repr. as Essai genres Famille Thalassio-
    phytes non articulées 57, 1813.
  P. variegata Hauck, Hedwigia 26: 42, 1887.
  Zonaria variegata (Lamx.) Martius, Icon. Pl. Cryptog. 6, pl.
    2, fig. 2, 1827.
  P. variegata (Lamx.) Hauck sensu Børg., Dansk Bot. Arkiv
    1(2): 205, 1914; 2(2): 49, 1914.
  See Taxon 3: 234, 1954; 4: 118, 1955.

780. *Panicum paludosum* Hassk., Pl. Jav. Rar. 16-17, 1848.
  P. paludosum Roxb., Hort. Beng. 8, 1814; Fl. Ind. 1: 307,
    1832.

781. *Clerodendron canescens* Wall., Cat. (Num. List Pl. E. Ind.)
    No. 1,804, 1828-1849; Wall. in Schauer in DC., Prodr.
    11: 665, 1847.

782. *Cyrtandra* J. R. & G. Forst., Char. Gen. 5-6, pl. 3, 1776.
  Kyrtandra Blanco, Fl. Filip. 18, 1837.
  Getonia Banks & Soland. ex Benn., Pl. Jav. Rar. 122, 1838.
  Rhynchocarpus Reinw. & Bl., Cat. Gew. Buitenzorg 84,
    1823.
  Whitia Bl., Cat. Gew. Buitenzorg 16-17, 1823.

783. *Rhynchospora glauca* Vahl form 2 *condensata* Kükenth. in
    Engler, Bot. Jahrb. 69(2): 259, 1938; Engler Bot. Jahrb.
    75: 148, 1950.

784. *Perispermon* Heydr., West. Ausbau Corall. Syst., Deutsch.
    Bot. Ges., Ber. 18: 316, 1900.
  Perispermum Degener, Fl. Haw. 307: 8/10/'32.

785. *Styphelia Tameiameiae* (Cham.) F. Muell., Fragm. Phytogr.
     Austral. 6: 57, 1867.
     Cyathodes Tameiameiae Cham., Linnaea 1: 539, 1826.

786. *Canavalia* ? *galeata* Gaud., Bot. Voy. Freyc. Uranie 486,
     (1826) = [1830].
     C. galeata (Gaud.) Gaud. ex Vogel, Linnaea 10: 584, 1836.
     Dolichos galeatus Gaud., Bot. Voy. Freyc. Uranie 486,
     (1826) = [1830]; Atlas pl. 115, 1826.
       See St. John, Bishop Mus., Occas. Pap. 15(22): 231-233,
       1940.

787. *Rhinanthus minor* L. ssp. *borealis* (Sterneck) Löve, Bot.
     Notis. 1950(1): 52, 1950.

788. *Inocarpus* J. R. & G. Forst., Char. Gen. 65-66, pl. 33, 1776.
     Bocoa Aubl., Hist. Pl. Guiane 2: Suppl, 38, 1775; 4: pl.
     391, 1775.
     Etballia Benth., Hooker's Jour. Bot. 2: 99, 1840.
   · *Inodaphnis* Miq., Fl. Ind. Bat. Suppl. 357, 1861.
     Inocarpus fagiferus (Parkins.) Fosb., Wash. Acad. Sci.,
     Jour. 31: 95-96, 1941.

789. *Epipremnum humile* (Schott) Hook. f., Fl. Brit. Ind. 6: 549,
     1893.
     Anadryum humile Schott in Miq., Mus. Bot. Lugd. Bat. 1:
     127, 1893.

790. *Desmos cochinchinensis* Lour., Fl. Cochinchin. 352, 1790.
     D. chinensis Lour., Fl. Cochinchin. 352, 1790.
       See Furtado, Gardens' Bull. 9: 226, 1937.
         Merrill, Am. Phil. Soc., Trans. 24(2): 160-161, 1935.

791. *Cyrtandra Clarkei* Vatke forma *ovatifolia* Skottsb., Hort.
     Gotoburg., Acta 15: 444, 1944.

792. *Oenothera argillicola* Mackenzie, Torreya 4: 56-57, 1904.
     Onagra argillicola Mackenzie, Torreya 4: 57, 1904.

793. *Persoonia coriacea* Audas, Australian Bushland 131, 1950.

794. *Pterula brunneosetosa* Corner, Ann. Bot. n. s. 16(64): 535,
     fig. 1, 1952.

795. *Scirpus swampianus* Bosc ex Kunth, Enum. Pl. 2: 168, 1837.

796. *Delphinium occidentale* Wats., Bot. Calif, 2: 428, 1880.
     D. elatum L. var. (?) *occidentale* Wats., Bot. King. Exped.
     11, 1871.

D. occidentale (Wats.) Wats., Ewan, Univ. Colo. Stud., ser.
   D, 2(2): 136–138, 1945.

797. *Halymenia Durvillaei* Bory var. *formosa* Weber van Bosse,
   Siboga Exped., Monogr. 59b: 235, 1921.
   H. formosa Kütz., Tab. Phyc. 16: 33, pl. 91, g, h, 1866.

798. *Salvia afr. lutea* L., Sp. Pl. 26, 1753.
   S. aurea L., Sp. Pl., ed. 2, 1: 38, 1762.

799. *Silphium terebinthinaceum* Jacq. var. *Lucy-Brauniae*
   Steyerm., Rhodora 53: 134, 1951.

800. *Rhus Filicina* Moç. & Sessé ex DC., Prodr. 2: 67, 1825.
   R. potentillaefolia Turcz., Soc. Nat. Mosc., Bul. 31: 469,
      1858.
   R. Tetlatziam Sessé & Moç., Pl. Nov. Esp. 47, 1887; ed. 2,
      44, xi, 1893.
   Toxicodendron potentillifolium Ktze., Rev. Gen. Pl. 1:
      154, 1891.
   Actinocheita filicina (DC.) Barkley, Mo. Bot. Gard., Ann.
      24: 2–5, 1937.
      See Barkley & Reed, Am. Midl. Nat. 21: 368–377, 1939.
         Bullock, Kew Bul. 337–339, 1939.
         Furtado, Gardens' Bul. 12: 367–368, 1949.

801. *Pinus monophyllus* Torr. & Frém. in Frém., Rept. Expl.
   Exped. Rocky Mts. 319, pl. 4, 1845.
   P. cembrodes Zucc. var. *monophylla* (Torr. & Frém.) Voss,
      Deut. Gardenrat Beilage 123, 1904; Deut. Dendrol.
      Gesell., Mitt. 16: 95, 1907.
   Caryopitys monophylla (Torr. & Frém.) Rydb., Torrey Bot.
      Club, Bul. 32: 597, 1905.

802. *Robinia PseudoAcacia* L., Sp. Pl. 722, 1753.
   R. Pseud-Acacia L. emend. L., Sp. Pl., ed. 2: 1,043–1,044,
      1763.

803. *Fimbristylis cymosa* R. Br. var. *pycnocephala* Kükenth. in
   Skottsb., Göteborg Bot. Trädgård, Meddel. 2: 212,
   1926.
   F. pycnocephala Hbd., Fl. Haw. Is. 473–474, 1888.

804. *Inga urabensis* L. Uribe, Caldasia 4: 406, 1947.

805. *Saxifraga occidentalis* Wats. var. *wallowensis* Peck, Leafl.
   W. Bot. 5: 60, 1947.

806. *Quercus virginiana* Mill. var. *eximea* Sarg., Bot. Gaz. 65:
447, 1918.

Q. virginiana Mill. var. *eximia* Sarg. emend. Dayton in
Little, Check List Native Nat. Trees of U. S. 247,
1944; Rhodora 54: 77, 1952.

807. *Triticum* L., Gen. Pl., ed. 5, 37, 1754.

Tritica L., Sp. Pl. 85, 1753.

808. *Glossopetalum* Schreb., Gen. Pl. of Linnaeus, ed. 8 by
Schreb., 1: 205, 1789.

Glossopetalon Gray, Pl. Wright. 2: 29, pl. 123, 1853.

Forsellesia Greene, Erythea 1: 206, 1893.

See Ensign, Am. Midl. Nat. 27: 501–511, 1942.

St. John, Biol. Soc. Wash., Proc. 55: 109–112, 1942.

809. *Cloëzia* Brongn. & Gris., Soc. Bot. France, Bul. 10: 576–
577, 1863.

810. *Calceolaria Storkii* Standl., Field. Mus. Nat. Hist., Bot.
Ser., Publ. 18(3): 1,103, 1938.

811. *Canthium barbatum* (Forst. f.) Seem. var. *australense* Fosb.
forma *tubuai* Fosb., Bishop Mus., Occas. Pap. 13(19):
259, 1937.

812. *Aconitum variegatum* L. β *typicum* Regel, Ann. Sci. Nat.
Bot. IV, 16: 147, 1862.

A. variegatum L. α *Canarum* (Reichb.) Regel in Reichb.,
Ill. Gen. Acon. pl. 34, 1823–27.

813. *Amaryllis Bella donna* L., Sp. Pl. 293, 1753.

A. Belladonna L. emend. L., Sp. Pl., ed. 2, 1: 421, 1763.

See Traub & Moldenke, Amaryllidaceae, 1949.

Dyer, Taxon 3: 72–74, 1954.

Dandy & Fosberg, Taxon 3: 231–232, 1954.

814. *Arnica Lessingii* (T. & G.) Greene, Pittonia 4: 167, 1900.

A. angustifolia H. & A. β *Lessingii* T. & G., Fl. N. Am. 2:
449, 1843.

A. alpina (L.) Olin & Ladau var. *Lessingii* Gray, Syn. Fl. N.
Am. 1(2): 383, 1884.

A. Porsildiorum Boivin, Nat. Canad. 75: 210, 1949.

See Rydberg, N. Am. Fl. 34: 328, 1927.

Maguire, Rhodora 52: 281–283, 1950.

Boivin, Rhodora 55: 57, 1953.

815. *Cyperus odoratus* L., Sp. Pl. 46, 1753.

    C. Ferax L. C. Rich., Soc. Hist. Nat. Paris, Act. 1: 106, 1792.

      See Clarke, Linn. Soc. Lond., Jour. 30: 306–307, 1895.

        Kükenthal, in Engler's Pflanzenreich IV, 20(4): 624, 1936.

816. *Capparis cynophallophora* L., Sp. Pl. 504, 1753.

    C. Jamaicensis Jacq., Enum. Pl. Carib. 23, 1760.

    C. cynophallophora L., Syst. Nat., ed. 10, 2: 1,071, 1759.

    C. flexuosa L., Sp. Pl., ed. 2, 722, 1763.

      See Small, Man. S. E. Fl. 577, 1933.

817. *Polypodium vulgare* L. monstr. *acuminatum* Copel., Bot. Gaz. 34: 143–144, 1902.

    P. vulgare acuminatum Copel., Bot. Gaz. 34: 143, fig. 4–5, 1902.

818. *Goniophlebium* Presl, Tent. Pterid. 185, pl. 7, fig. 13–14, 1836.

      See Copeland, Gen. Fil. 181, 1947.

        Furtado, Lloydia 12: 72, 1949.

819. *Cyphokentia samoensis* Warb. in Reinecke, Engler's Bot. Jahrb. 25: 588, 1898.

      See Furtado, Gardens' Bul. 9: 291, 1937.

820. *Smilax Pseudo-China* L., Sp. Pl. 1,031, 1753.

    S. tamnoides L., Sp. Pl. 1,030, 1753.

    S. tamnifolia Michx., Fl. Bor.-Am. 2: 238, 1803.

      See Fernald, Rhodora 46: 32–35, 1944.

821. *Anapausia* Presl, Epim. Bot. 185, 1849.

      See Copeland, Gen. Fil. 132, 1947.

822. *Boerhavia diffusa* L., Sp. Pl. 3, 1753.

      See Heimerl, Bishop Mus., Occas. Pap. 13(4): 28, 1937.

823. *Apera* Adans., Fam. Pl. 2: 495, 1763.

    Agrostis L., Sp. Pl. 61–63, 1753; Gen. Pl., ed. 5, 30, 1754.

824. *Rhynchosia difformis* DC., Prodr. 2: 384, 1825.

    Arcyphyllum Difforme Ell., Acad. Nat. Sci. Phila., Jour. 1: 371–372, 1818.

      See Gleason, Phytologia 2: 212, 1947.

825. *Asplenium nidus* L., Sp. Pl. 1,079, 1753.
Ophrys Nidus avis L., Sp. Pl. 945, 1753.

826. *Astragalus Punjabicus* Sirajaev, Brittonia 7: 275-276, 1951.
Onobrychis ralphii Sirajaev, Brittonia 7: 275, 1951.
Astragalus Albus Sirajaev, Brittonia 7: 276, 1951.
A. hircina Jacq. var. *indica* Sirajaev, Brittonia 7: 276-277, 1951.

827. *Asystasia* Bl., Bijdr. Fl. Nederl. Ind. 796, (1825) = [1826].

828. *Barbarea barbarea* (L.) MacMillan, Minn. Geol. & Nat. Hist. Surv., Bot. Ser., Rept. 1: 259, 1892.
Erysimum Barbarea L., Sp. Pl. 660, 1753.
Barbarea vulgaris R. Br. in Ait., Hort. Kew., ed. 2, 4: 109, 1812.

829. *Beautempsia* Gaud., Bot. Voy. La Bonite pl. 56, (1844-1866) =[1842].

830. *Bernardia Bernardia* (L.) Millsp., Field Columb. Mus., Bot. 2: 58, 1900.
Bernardia carpinifolia Griseb., Fl. Brit. W. I. 45, 1864.
B. dichotoma Muell. Arg. α *genuina* Muell. Arg., Linnaea 34: 172, 1865-1866.
Adelia Bernardia (P. Browne) L., Syst. Nat., ed. 10, 1,298, 1759.

831. *Brunfelsia mire* Monachino, Phytologia 4: 342-347, 1953.

832. *Clematis pseudoscabiosaefolia* Perrier de la Bathie forma *normalis* Perrier de la Bathie, Mus. Natl. Hist. Nat. Paris, Not. Syst. 14(4): 309, 1952.

833. *Trematosphaeria Morthieri* Fuckel, Nassau Ver. Naturk., Jahrb. 25-26: 306, 1871; Symb. Myc. Nacht. 1: 306, 1871.
Zignoella Morthieri (Fuckel) Sacc., Michelia 1: 347, 1878; Syll. Fung. 2: 222, 1883.
Clypeothecium Weirii Petrak, Ann. Myc. 20: 182, 1922.
Trematostoma Morthieri (Fuckel) Shear, Mycologia 270, 1942.

834. *Crescentia* L., Gen. Pl., ed. 5, 274, 1754.

835. *Cucurbita* L., Gen. Pl., ed. 5, 441, 1754; Sp. Pl. 1,010-1,011, 1753.

Cucurbita L., Mill., Gard. Dict., ed. 8, Cucurbita, 1768.
Lagenaria Ser., Soc. Phys. Genêve, Mem. 3(1): 25-26, pl.
2, 1825; Ser. in DC., Mem. 3: 417, 1881.
Pepo [Tourn.] Mill., Gard. Dict., abr. ed. 4, Pepo, 1754.
See Britton & Brown, Ill. Fl. N. U. S., ed. 2, 3: 291,
1913.
Bailey, Gent. Herb. 2(2): 78-81, 1929; 2(7): 427-430,
1932.

836. *Polemonium occidentale* Greene, Pittonia 2: 75, 1890.
P. caeruleum L. ssp. *occidentale* (Greene) J. F. Davidson,
Univ. Calif., Publ. Bot. 23(5): 225, 1950.
See Brand in Engler, Pflanzenreich IV, 250: 33, 1907.

837. *Hernandia labyrinthica* Tuyama, Sigenkagaku Kenkyusyo,
Bul. 1(1): 42-44, 2 pl., 1943.

838. *Trichomanes* L., Gen. Pl., ed. 5, 485, 1754; Sp. Pl. 1,097-
1,099, 1753.
Vandenboschia Copel., Philip. Jour. Sci. 67: 51, 1937.
See Holttum, Gardens' Bul. 12: 304-305, 1937.

839. *Polygala verticillata* L., Sp. Pl. 706, 1753.
See Fernald, Rhodora 40: 334-338, 1938.
Pennell, Rhodora 41: 378-384, 1939.

840. *Cyclomycetella pavonia* (Hook.) Murrill, Torrey Bot. Club,
Bul. 31: 423, 1904.
Polyporus iodinus Mont., Ann. Sci. Nat. Bot. II, 16: 108,
1841.
P. striatus Mont., Ann. Sci. Nat. Bot. II, 13: 205, 1840.
Cycloporellus iodinus (Mont.) Murrill, Torrey Bot. Club,
Bul. 34: 468, 1907; N. Am. Fl. 9(2): 85, 1908.
See Donk, Reinwardtia 1: 485, 1952.

841. *Cynodon Dactylon* (L.) Pers., Syn. Pl. 1: 85, 1805.
Panicum dactylon L., Sp. Pl. 58, 1753.
Dactylon R. & S., Syst. Veg. of Linnaeus, ed. 9 by R. &
S., 2: 411, 1817.
Dactilon Vill., Hist. Pl. Dauph. 2: 69, 1787.

842. *Cyperus Papyrus* L., Sp. Pl. 47, 1753.

843. *Cyrtandra olona* C. N. Forbes, Bishop Mus., Occas. Pap.
8(3): 34, pl. 5, 1920.

844. *Destrugesia* Gaud., Bot. Voy. La Bonite pl. 57, (1844-1866) = [1842].

Destruguezia Gaud. ex B. & H., Gen. Pl. 1: 109, 1862.

845. *Didymella Ilicis* Larsen, Dansk Bot. Arkiv 14(7): 21-22, 1952.

846. *Eleocharis capitata* R. Br., Prodr. Fl. Nov. Holl. 1: 225, 1810.

   Scirpus capitatus L., Sp. Pl. 48, 1753.

   S. capitatus Willd., Sp. Pl. of Linnaeus, ed. 4 by Willd., 1: 294, 1797.

   See Clarke, Linn. Soc. Lond. Bot., Jour. 30: 310, 1894.

   Blake, Rhodora 20: 24, 1918.

   Farwell, Rhodora 32: 180-181, 1930.

   Furtado, Gardens' Bul. 9: 293-294, 1937.

847. *Solidago ulmifolia* Muhl. var. *Palmeri* Cronq. in Gleason, New Britton & Brown Ill. Fl. N. E. U. S. & Can. 3: 428, 1952.

   S. ulmifolia Muhl. var. *palmeri* Cronq., Rhodora 57: 36, 1955.

848. *Schmidtia* Moench, Meth. Pl. Hort. Marburg., Suppl. 217, 1802.

   Schmidtia Tratt., Fl. Austr. 1: 12-13, pl. 451, 1816.

   Schmidtia Steud. in J. A. Schmidt, Beitr. Fl. Cap. Verd. Ins. 144-146, 1852.

   Schmidia Wight, Icon. Pl. Ind. Orient. 16, pl. 1,848, 1852.

849. *Halymenia Durvillaei* Bory var. *edentata* Weber-van Bosse, Siboga Exped., Monogr. 59b: 236, 1921.

850. *Hibiscus caerulescens* Baill. var. *Humbertiellus* Hochr., Candollea 12: 176, 1949.

   Perrierophytum Humbertianthus Hochr., Candollea 12: 181, 1949.

   Humbertiella Pseudohenrici Hochr., Candollea 12: 185, 1949.

851. *Hibiscus mandrarensis* Humbert in schedulis, Hochr., spec. nov. (e § *Lilibiscus*), Candollea 12: 175, 1949.

852. *Lagenifera* Cass., Soc. Philom. Paris, Bul. Sci. 199, 1816.

   Lagenofera Cass., Soc. Philom. Paris, Bul. Sci. 34, 1818.

   See Davis, Linn. Soc. N. S. W., Proc. 75: 122, 1950.

853. *Leiacina* Raf., Neogenyton 4, 1825.

 Tolypella A. Braun, Fragm. Monogr. Charac., ed. Norstedt, 93, 1882.

  See Wood, Torrey Bot. Club, Bul. 75: 283, 1948.

854. *Matricaria matricarioides* (Less.) Porter, Torrey Bot. Club, Mem. 5: 341, 1894.

 Artemisia matricarioides Less., Linnaea 6: 210, 1831.

 Matricarioides Less., Linnaea 6: 210, 1831.

 Matricarioides Spach, Hist. Vég. Phan. 10: 24, 1841.

855. *Meliola gregoriana* Stevens, Bishop Mus., Bul. 19: 39, 1925.

 M. forbesii Stevens, Bishop Mus., Bul. 19: 29, 1925.

856. *Pachypodium* Nutt. ex T. & G., Fl. N. Am. 1: 96, 1838.

857. *Phaius* Lour., Fl. Cochinch. 529, 1790.

 Phajus Hassk., Cat. Pl. Hort. Bog., ed. alt., 41–42, 1844.

  See Rickett, Taxon 4: 185–188, 1955.

858. *Polypodium Dryopteris* L. β *P. Robertianum* Hoffm. ex Hook. & Bak., Syn. Fil. 309, 1874.

 P. Robertianum Hoffm., Deutschl. Fl. 2: unnumbered 231st. page, 1796.

859. *Pothuava* Gaud., Bot. Voy. La Bonite pl. 116–117, (1844–1866) =[1851].

860. *Silene antirrhina* L., Sp. Pl. 419, 1753.

 S. Antirrhina L., C. L. Hitchc. & Maguire, Univ. Wash., Publ. Biol. 13: 14, 1947.

861. *Tacca maculata* Zipp. ex Span., Linnaea 15: 480, 1841.

 T. maculata Seem., Fl. Vit. 103, 1865.

862. *Vilfoidea* (Rouy) Beetle, Univ. Wyo., Publ. 15(2): 32, 1950.

 Vilfoidea Rouy, Fl. France 14: 59, 1913.

863. *Columellia* Ruiz & Pavon, Fl. Peruv. Prodr. 3, pl. 1, 1794.

864. *Sarmienta* Ruiz & Pavon, Fl. Peruv. Prodr. 4, 1794.

865. *Sanchezia* Ruiz & Pavon, Fl. Peruv. Prodr. 5, pl. 32, 1794.

866. *Schizanthus* Ruiz & Pavon, Fl. Peruv. Prodr. 6, 1794.

867. *Senecio Guadalupe* Cuatr., Fieldiana Bot. 27(2): 23, 1951.

868. *Ulmus rubra* Muhl., Am. Phil. Soc., Trans. 3: 165, 1793.

 U. fulva Michx., Fl. Bor.-Am. 1: 172, 1803.

  See Fernald, Rhodora 47: 203–204, 1945.

869. *Cyrtandra Taitensis* Rich ex Gray, Am. Acad. Arts Sci.,
Proc. 6: 39, 1866.
C. tahitensis Nad., Enum. Pl. Tahiti 60, 1873.
C. Nadeaudi C. B. Clarke, in DC., Monogr. 5(1): 264–265,
1883.

870. *Triumfetta* L., Gen. Pl., ed. 5, 203, 1754; Sp. Pl. 444, 1753.

871. *Euphorbia Celastroides* Boiss. var. *Odonatoides* Sherff, Am.
Jour. Bot. 38: 55, fig. 2, 1951.

872. *Crateva* L., Gen. Pl., ed. 5, 203, 1754; Sp. Pl., ed. 2, 636–
637, 1762.
Crataeva L., Gen. Pl., ed. 5, index, 1754; ed. 6, 238, 1764;
Syst. Nat., ed. 13, 2: 326, 1770.
Crataeua L., Syst. veg. of Linnaeus, ed. 13 by Gmelin,
index, 1770.
See Rickett, Taxon 4: 185–188, 1955.

873. *Bellonia* L., Gen. Pl., ed. 5, 79, 1754; Sp. Pl. 172, 1753.

874. *Rhynchospora pseudo-Sellowiana* Kükenth., Bot. Jahrb. 75:
155, 1950.
R. Sellowiana Steud., Nom., ed. 2, 2: 456, 1841; Syn. Pl.
Cyp. 145, 1855.
R. Selloiana Boeck., Linnaea 37: 620, 1871–1873.
R. filifolia Kunth, Enum. Pl. 2: 299, 1837.
R. filifolia Gray in Torr., Lyc. Nat. Hist. New York, Ann.
3: 366, 1836.

875. *Juglans microcarpa* Berland. in Berland. & Chovel, Diario
Viage Comision de Limites bajo Mier y Teran 276,
1850.
J. rupestris Engelm. ex Torr. in Sitgreaves, Rept. Exped.
Zuni & Colo. Rivers 171, pl. 15, 1853. (32nd. U. S.
Congr. Senate, Exec. No. 59).
J. nana Engelm., Am. Assoc. Adv. Sci., Proc. 5: 226, 1851.
J. Whippleana Bigel. ex Engelm. in Sitgreaves, Rept. Exped.
Exped. Zuni & Colo. Rivers 171, 1853.
See Johnson, Jour. Arn. Arb. 25: 436, 1944.

876. *Monarda punctata* L. ssp. *villicaulis* Pennell, Torrey Bot.
Club, Bul. 46: 186, 1919.
M. punctata L. ssp. *villicaulis* (Pennell) Epling. Madroño
3: 24, 1935.

M. *punctata* L. var. *villicaulis* Pennell ex Palmer &
Steyerm., Mo. Bot. Gard., Ann. 22: 634, 1935.
M. *punctata* L. var. *villicaulis* (Pennell) Shinners, Field &
Lab. 21: 90, 1953.

877. *Baccharis cundinamarcenssis* Cuatr., Mutisia 17: 4, 1953.

878. *Bupariti* Duhamel, Sem. Pl. Arbres, Addit. 5, 1760.
Thespesia Soland. ex Correa, Mus. Paris, Ann. 9: 290, pl.
8, fig. 2, 1807.
See Rothmaler, Fedde Repert. 53: 6–7, 1944.
Taxon 3: 118, 156, 233, 1954.

879. *Aconitum fudjipedis* Nakai, Natl. Sci. Mus. (Tokyo), Bul.
32: 28, 1953.

880. *Stenoloma* Fée, Gen. Fil. or Mém. Fam. Foug. 5: 203, 330,
(1850–1852) = [1852].
See Pichi-Sermolli, Webbia 9: 361–362, 1953; Taxon 3:
71, 1954.

881. *Ilex Paraguariensis* St.-Hil., Mus. Hist. Nat. Paris, Mém. 9:
351, 1822.
I. Mate St.-Hil., Hist. Pl. Remarq. Brésil & Parag. 1: xli,
1824.
I. Curitivensis Miers, Ann. Mag. Nat. Hist. III, 8: 393–394,
1861; repr. as Hist. Maté Pl. 14–15, 1861.
I. Paraguariensis St.-Hil. var. α *genuina* Loes., Monogr.
Aquifol. 1: 304–306, 1901.
See Parold & Grondona, Revista Argent. Agron. 16: 199–
204, fig. 1–2, 1949.

882. *Astragalus mollissimus earlei* (Greene) Tidestrom, Biol.
Soc. Wash., Proc. 48: 40, 1935.
A. Earlei Greene in Rydb., N. Am. Fl. 24(7): 444, 1929.
A. Humboldtii sensu M. E. Jones, Rev. Astragal. 232, 1923,
non Gray (1864).

883. *Althaea foliis simplicibus acuminatis acuté dentatis
tomentosis* Mill., Gard. Dict., ed. 8, Althaea No. 1,
1768.

884. *Veronica catenata* Pennell, Rhodora 23: 37, 1921.
V. connata glaberrima Pennell, Scrophı E. Temp. N. Am.
368–370, 1935.

V. comosa Richter var. *glaberrima* (Pennell) Boivin, Nat.
Canad. 79: 174, 1952.

885. *Capparis cordifolia* Lam., Encyc. Méth. Bot. 1: 609, 1785.
C. mariana Jacq., Pl. Rar. Hort. Caes. Schoenbrunn. Descr.
Icon. 1: 57, pl. 109, 1797.
Blumea grandiflora Zipp. ex Spanoghe, Linnaea 15: 165,
1841; Miq., Fl. Nederl. Ind. 1(2): 100, 1860.
C. spinosa L. var. *Mariana* (Jacq.?) K. Schum., Engler Bot.
Jahrb. 9: 201, 1888; Schum. & Lauterb., Fl. Deut.
Schutzgeb. 335, 1901.

886. *Aponogeton oblongus* Troupin, Jard. Bot. État Bruxelles,
Bul. 23(3-4): 224-225, 1953.

887. *Sorbus americana* Marsh., Arbust. Am. 145, 1785.
S. americana Pursh, Fl. Am. Sept. 1: 341, 1814.
S. micrantha Dum.-Cours., Bot. Cult., ed. 2, 5: 464, 1811.
S. microcarpa Pursh, Fl. Am. Sept. 1: 341, 1814.
Pyrus microcarpa (Pursh) DC., Prodr. 2: 636-637, 1825.
Pyrus americana (Pursh) DC., Prodr. 2: 637, 1825.
See Jones, Rhodora 55: 358-360, 1953.

888. *Apionema obovatum* Nutt., Hillebrand, Fl. Haw. Is. 179,
1888.
Straussia Kaduana (C. & S.) Gray, Am. Acad. Arts Sci.,
Proc. 4: 43, 1860.
Coffea Kaduana C. & S., Linnaea 4: 33, 1829.

889. *Berberis canadensis* Pursh, Fl. Am. Sept. 219, 1814.
See Fernald, Rhodora 44: 31, 1942.

890. *Potentilla pensylvanica* L., Mant. 1: 76, 1767.
See Fernald, Rhodora 44: 31, 1942.

891. *Drosera longifolia* L., Sp. Pl. 282, 1753.
D. anglica Huds., Fl. Angl., ed. 2, 135, 1778.
D. intermedia Hayne, in Schrader's Neues Jour. 3(1): 37-39,
1800.
See Diels, in Engler, Pflanzenreich IV, fam. 112: 83-84,
96-97, 1906.

892. *Eupatorium Benjamin-Lincolnii* Steyerm., Fieldiana Bot.
28(3): 635, 1953.

893. *Euphorbia* (bezw. **Chamaesyce** [*nutans* var.?] **pseudo-nutans**
Thell. in Aschers. & Graebn., Syn. Mitteleurop. Fl.
7(92): 431, 1917.

894. *Blumea* (an *Pluchea* ?) *somaliensis* Thell., Zürich Naturf.
Gesell., Vierteljahrsschr. 68: 443–444, 1923.

895. *Sida paniculata* L., Syst. Nat., ed. 10, 2: 1,145, 1760.
S. panniculata L. ex. K. Schum. in Mart., Fl. Brasil. 12(3):
293, 1891.

896. *Urera Bequaertii* de Wild. in herb. ex Hauman, in Fl. Congo
Belge & Ruanda-Urundi 1: 184, 1948.

897. *Sassafras Tzumu* (Hemsley) Hemsley, Kew Bul. 55, 1907.
Lindera Tzumu Hemsl., Linn. Soc. Lond. Bot., Jour. 26:
392, 1891.
Litsea laxiflora Hemsl., Linn. Soc. Lond., Bot., Jour. 26:
383, pl. 8, 1891.
Lindera laxiflora Hemsl. ex Lecomte, Mus. Paris, Nouv.
Archiv V, 5: 117, 1913.
Pseudosassafras Tzumu (Hemsl.) Lecomte, Not. Syst. 2:
269, 1911.
P. laxiflora (Hemsl.) Nakai, Jour. Jap. Bot. 16: 126, 1940.
See Keng, Taiwan Mus., Quart. Jour. 6: 78–85, 2 pl. 1953.

898. *Gouldia terminalis* (H. & A.) Hbd. var. *antiqua* Fosb. forma
kauensis Fosb., Bishop Mus., Bul. 147: 55, 1937.

899. *Carex mund* Boott var. *mundaeformis* Koyama, Acta Phy-
totax. Geobot. 15(4): 113, 1954.

900. *Gouania Hillebrandi* Oliver in Hbd., Fl. Haw. Is. 83, 1888.
Pleuranthodes Hillebrandti (Oliver) Weberb. in Engler &
Prantl, Nat. Pflanzenfam. IV, 3(5): 424, 1896.
P. hillebrandii (Oliver) Weberb. ex Suessenguth, Engler &
Prantl, Nat. Pflanzenfam., ed. 2, 20d: 166, 1953.
Lupulus orbicularis Ktze., β *Hillebrandtii* (Oliver) Ktze.,
Rev. Gen. Pl. 1: 119, 1891.

901. *Dalea enneandra* Nutt., in Fraser's Cat. 1813; repr., Pit-
tonia 2: 117, 1890.
D. laxiflora Pursh, Fl. Am. Sept. 2: 741, 1814.
See Shinners, Rhodora 57: 290–293, 1955;
Cronquist *et al.*, Rhodora 58: 23–24, 1956;

Cronquist, Rhodora 59: 100, 1957;
Shinners, Rhodora 58: 281–289, 1956;
Graustein, Rhodora 58: 20–22, 1956.

902. *Rhopalanthus* Lindb., Notis. Sällskap. Pro Fauna & Fl.
Fennica, Förhandl. 13: 390–391, 1874.
Rhossalanthus mnioides Lindb. in Austin, Torrey Bot.
Club, Bul. 6: 21, 1875.
Rhopalanthus Lindb. in Austin, Torrey Bot. Club, Bul. 6:
304, 1879.

903. *Pteris ternifolia* Cav., Descr. Pl. 266, 1802.
Pellaea ternifolia (Cav.) Link, Fil. Sp. Hort. Bot. Berol.
59, 1841.

904. *Sida Meyeniana* Walp., Rel. Meyen., Acad. Caes. Leop.-
Carol. Nat. Curios., Nov. Act. 16: suppl 2: 307, 1842.
S. Meyeniana Walp. α var. *genuina* Hochr., Conserv. & Jard.
Bot. Genève, Ann. 6: 39, 1902.
Anoda ovata Meyen, Reise Erde Prinzess Louise 2: 139,
1835.

905. *Sida lepida* F. Muell., Fragm. Phytograph. Austral. 6: 168,
1868.
S. lepidota Gray, Pl. Wright. 18, 1852.

906. *Crescentia Cujete* L., Sp. Pl. 626, 1753.
Cuiete Adans., Fam. Pl. 2: 207, 1763.

907. *Bergia capensis* L., Mant. 2: 241, 1771.

908. *Suaeda* Forsk., Fl. Aegypt.-Arab. 69–71, 1775; Niebuhr,
Icon. Rerum Natur. pl. 18B, 1776.
Dondia Adans., Fam. Pl. 2: 261, 1763.
Lerchea Hall., Hort. Goett. 21, 1743; Rueling, Ord. Pl. 45,
1774.
Cochliospermum Lag., Mem. Pl. Barill. 55, 1817.
Belowia Moq. in DC., Prodr. 13(2): 168, 1849.
Suaeda vermiculata Forsk., Fl. Aegypt.-Arab. 70, 1775;
Forsk. ex J. F. Gmel., Syst. Nat. of Linnaeus, ed. 13
by J. F. Gmel., 2: 503, 1791.
See Uster, Delect. Opusc. Bot. 2: 460, 1793.
Brenan, Taxon 3: 65, 1954.
Burtt & Lewis, Kew Bul. 387, 1954.

909. *Microoecia* Hook. f., Linn. Soc. Lond., Proc. 1: 278, 1849.

910. *Passiflora mariquitensis* Mutis ex Uribe, Mutisia 21: 1-5, pl. 1, 1954.

911. *Lithospermum incanum* Forst. f., Fl. Ins. Austral. Prodr. 12, 1786.

Heliotropium anomalum H. & A., Bot. Beechey Voy. 66, 1832.

H. incanum (Forst. f.) Skottsb., Göteborg. Bot. Trädgård, Meddel. 2: 259, 1926.

912. *Panicum affine* H. & A., Bot. Beechey Voy. 100, 1841.

P. affine Poir. in Lam., Encyc. Méth. Bot. Suppl. 4: 273, 1816.

P. lanaiense Hitchc., Bishop Mus., Mem. 8(3): 189, 1922.

P. Colliei Endl., Wien. Mus. Naturgesch., Ann. 1: 157, 1836.

913. *Daedalacanthus nervosus* (Vahl) T. Anders., Linn. Soc. Lond., Jour. 9: 487, 1867.

Justicia nervosa Vahl, Enum. Pl. 1: 164, 1804.

Eranthemum nervosum (Vahl) R. Br. ex R. & S., Syst. Veg. of Linnaeus, ed. nov. by R. & S., 1: 174, 1817.

E. pulchellum Andrews, Bot. Reposit. 2: pl. 88, [1798].

See Fosberg, Taxon 2(6): 135-136, 1953.

914. *Citharexylum spinosum* L., Sp. Pl. 625, 1753.

See Britton & Wilson, New York Acad. Sci., Sci. Surv. Porto Rico 6: 146, 1925.

915. *Duckera* Barkley, Am. Midl. Nat. 28: 472, 1942.

Rhus, sect. *Melanocarpae* Engler, Bot. Jahrb. 1: 380, 1881.

916. *Premna integrifolia* L., Mant. 2: 252, 1771.

P. serratifolia L., Mant. 2: 253, 1771.

Cornutia corymbosa Burm. f., Fl. Ind. 132, 1768.

P. corymbosa (Burm. f.) Rottl. & Willd. ex Merr., Int. Rumph. Herb. Amb. 450-451, 1917.

P. corymbosa Rottler, Ges. Naturf. Fr. Berlin, Neue Schr. 4: 187, 1803.

P. obtusifolia R. Br., Prodr. Fl. Nov. Holl. 512, 1810.

See Fosberg, Taxon 2(4): 88-89, 1953.

917. *Docanthe alba* O. F. Cook, Nat. Hort. Mag. (Am.) 22: 96, 150, 1943.

918. *Ipomaeella* A. Cheval., Rev. Bot. Appliq. 30: 272, 1950.

919. *Sechium* P. Browne, Civ. Nat. Hist. Jamaica 355, 1756.
Chocho Adans., Fam. Pl. 2: 500, 1763.
Chayota Jacq., Select. Am. ed. Pict. 124, pl. 245, 1780.

920. *Maerua oblongifolia* (Forsk.) Rich. var. *pallida* Pirota, Bruxelles Jard. Bot. État, Bul. 24(2): 138, 1954.

921. *Areca cathecu* L., Sp. Pl. 1,189, 1753.
A. Catechu Stickm., Herb. Amb. 6, 1754.
Mimosa Catechu L. f., Suppl. 439, 1781.

922. *Eichornia* Kunth, Enum. Pl. 4: 129–132, 1843.
Piaropus Raf., Fl. Tell. 2: 81, 1836.

923. *Lepidococcus* Wendl. & Druce in Kerchove de Denterghem, Les Palmiers, 249, in indice, 1878.
See Drude in Mart., Fl. Bras. 3(2): 292, 1881.
Hawkes, Bot. Est. Sao Paulo, Brasil, Arq. 2: 1–2, 1952.
Dugand, Mutisia 20: 1–2, 1954.

924. *Acer Wilsoni* Rehder in Sarg., Trees & Shrubs 157, pl. 79, 1902.
A. Wilsonii Rehd. emend. Lawrence, Baileya 2: 88, 1954.

925. *Peltophorum pterocarpum* (DC.) Backer ex K. Heyne, Nutt. Pl. Ned. Ind., ed. 2, 2: 755, 1927.
Inga pterocarpa DC., Prodr. 2: 441, 1825.
Caesalpinia inermis Roxb., Hort. Beng. 90, 1814.
Poinciana Roxburghii G. Don, Gen. Syst. 2: 433, 1832.
C. ferruginea Dcne., Mus. Paris, Nouv. Ann. 3: 462, 1834.
Peltophorum ferrugineum (Dcne.) Benth., Fl. Austral. 2: 279, 1864.
P. inerme (Roxb.) Naves in Blanco, Fl. Filip., ed. 3, pl. 335, 1877–1883.
Baryxylum inerme (Roxb.) Pierre, Fl. Forest. Cochinch. pl. 390, 1899.
Peltophorum Roxburghii (G. Don) Degener, Fl. Haw. 169b: 12/21/'38.
See Blake, Austral. Jour. Bot. 2: 112, 1954.

926. *Echites laxa* Ruiz & Pavon, Fl. Peruv. 2: 19, pl. 134, 1799.
  Mandevilla suaveolens Lindl., Edwards Bot. Reg. 26: pl.
     7, 1840.
  M. laxa (R. & P.) Woodson, Mo. Bot. Gard., Ann. 20: 695–
     696, 1933.
  Echites suaveolens (Lindl.) A. DC., Prodr. 8: 452, 1844.
  Amblyanthera suaveolens (Lindl.) Muell. Arg., Linnaea 30:
     447, 1860.
  M. Tweedieana Gadeceau & Stapf, Soc. Sci. Ouest Fr., Bul.
     III, 3: 2–3, 1913.

927. *Potentilla fruticosa* L., Sp. Pl. 495, 1753.
  Pentaphylloides fruticosa (L.) Schwarz, Thüring. Bot. Ges.,
     Mitt. 1: 105, 1949.
  Potentilla arbuscula D. Don, Prodr. Fl. Nepal. 256, 229–
     230, 1825.
  Pentaphylloides arbuscula (D. Don) Löve, Sv. Bot. Tidskr.
     48: 223, 1954.
  Dasiphora riparia Raf., Autikon Bot. 167, 1838.
  Potentilla Loureironis Tratt., Rosacearum Monogr. 4, 1824.
  Potentilla floribunda Pursh, Fl. Am. Sept. 355, 1814.
  Potentilla fruticosa L. forma *villosissima* Fern., Rhodora
     37: 292, 1935.
  Pentaphylloides floribunda (Pursh) Löve, Sv. Bot. Tidskr.
     48: 224, 1954.

928. *Alternanthera* Forsk., Fl. Aegypt.-Arab. 28, 1775.
  A. achyranth. Forsk., Fl. Aegypt.-Arab. 28, 1775.
  A. Achyrantha R. Br., Prodr. 1: 417 (or 273), 1810.

929. *Fissenia mentzeloides* R. Br. ex Harv., Thes. Cap. 1: 61,
     1859.
  Kissenia spathulata R. Br. ex T. Anders., Linn. Soc. Lond.,
     Jour. 5: Suppl. 1: 43, 1860.
  F. Capensis R. Br. ex Endl., Gen. Pl. Suppl. 2: 76, 1842;
     R. Br. ex Walp., Rep. 2: 228, 1843.
  Cnidone Mentzeloides E. Mey. ex Presl, K. Böhm. Ges.
     Wissensch., Abhandl. V, 3: 73, 1845; repr. as Bot.
     Bemerk. 73, 1845.

930. *Lactuca massaviensis* (Fresen.) Sch. Bip. ex A. Rich.,
     Tent. Fl. Abyss. 1: 460, 1847.

Brachyramphus lactucoides T. Anders., Linn. Soc. Lond.
Bot. 5: Suppl. 23, 1860.

Heterachaena massauensis Fresen., Mus. Senckenb. 3: 74,
1839.

931. *Scutellaria elliptica* Muhl., Am. Phil. Soc., Trans. 3: 173,
1793.

S. elliptica Mühl. ex Biehler, Pl. Nov. Herb. Spreng. Cent.
26, 1807.

S. elliptica Mühl. ex Spreng., Mant. Prim. Fl. Hal. 44, 1807.

S. integrifolia L., Sp. Pl. 599, 1753.

S. pilosa Michx., Fl. Bor.-Am. 2: 11, 1803.

S. ovalifolia Pers., Syn. Pl. 2: 136, (1807) = [1806].

S. nemorosa Raf., Am. Monthly Mag. II, 2: 120, 1817.

S. teucrifolia Sm., in Rees Cyclop. 32: Scutellaria No. 15,
1819.

S. pilosa Michx. β *ovalifolia* (Pers.) Benth. in DC., Prodr.
12: 423, 1848.

S. ovalifolia Pers. ssp. *mollis* Epling, Univ. Calif., Publ.
Bot. 20 (1): 86, 1942.

See Fernald, Rhodora 47: 200-203, 1945.

932. *Pandanus platyphyllus* Martelli, Webbia 2: 439, 1907; 4 (1):
27, 1913.

P. platiphyllus Martelli, Webbia 4 (2): pl. 28, fig. 34-37,
1914.

933. *Echites Echites* (L.) Britton in Small, Fl. Miami 147, 200,
1913.

Tabernaemontana Echites L., Syst. Nat., ed. 10, 2: 945.
1759.

934. *Ochrosia borbonica* J. F. Gmel., Syst. Nat. of Linnaeus, ed.
13 by J. F. Gmel., 2(1): 439, 1791.

Ochrosia Juss., Gen. Pl. 144-145, 1789.

O. maculata Jacq., Collect. 4: 218, 1790; Icon. Pl. Rar. 2:
pl. 321, 1792-1793.

Cerbera borbonica (Juss.) Spreng., Syst. Veg. of Linnaeus,
ed. 16 by Spreng., 1: 642, 1825.

C. maculata (Jacq.) Willd., Sp. Pl. of Linnaeus, ed. 4 by
Willd., 1 (2): 1,223, 1797.

C. platyspermos Gaertn., Fruct. 2: 193, pl. 124, fig. o-r, 1791.

C. undulata Andrews, Bot. Repos. pl. 130, 1798.

935. *Crataegus galbana* Beadle, Biltmore Bot. Stud. 1: 74, 1902.

C. pexa Beadle, Biltmore Bot. Stud. 1: 116, 1902.

C. senta Beadle, Bot. Gaz. 30: 341-342, 1900.

　　See R. M. Harper, Ala. Acad. Sci., Jour. 23-24: 134, 1953.

936. *Konig* Adans., Fam. Pl. 2: 23, 1763.

Koniga R. Br., in Denh. & Clapp., Narr. Exp. Afr. App. 214, 1826; repr. p. 9.

937. *Festuca Halleri* All., Fl. Ped. 2: 253, 1785.

938. *Gillespiea* A. C. Sm., Bishop Mus., Bul. 141: 158, 1936.

939. CLERODENDRUM CAPITATUM var. VANDERYSTI Moldenke, Phytologia 3: 407, 1950.

940. *Arisarum Libani* Schott, Prodr. Syst. Aroid. 21, 1860.

941. *Cyrtandra kalichii tristis* (Hbd.) Rock, Am. Jour. Bot. 6: 64-65, 1919.

942. *Robinia Caragana* L., Sp. Pl. 722, 1753.

943. *Fusicocum* Corda in Sturm, Deutschl. Fl. 3 abt., 1(9): 111, 1829.

944. *Zschokkea* Muell. Arg. in Mart., Fl. Bras. 6(1): 20, pl. 6, 7, 1860.

Zschokkia B. & H., Gen. Pl. 2: 694, 1876.

945. *Grifola Tuckahoe* Güss., Mycologia 11: 109, 1919.

946. *Hypnum gracile lancastriense* Sull. & Lesq., Musc. Bor. Am. 278, 1856.

947. *Braussonetia papyrifera* (L.) L'Her. ex Masamune, Kanazawa Univ., Sci. Rept. 2(2): 64, 1954; repr. as Enum. Tracheophyt. Ryukyu Ins. 4: 6, 1954.

Morus papyrifera L., Sp. Pl. 986, 1753.

Broussonetia papyrifera (L.) L'Her. ex Vent., Tabl. Regn. Veg. 3: 548, 1799.

Broussonetia secundiflora Ortega, Hort. Matr. 61-62, pl. 7, 1798.

948. *Philadelphus oreganus* Nutt. ex T. & G., Fl. N. Am. 1: 595, 1840.

See Hu, Jour. Arn. Arb. 36: 85, 1955.

949. *Swietenia Mahagoni* (L.) Jacq., Enum. Syst. Pl. Carib. 20, 1760; ed. 2, 20, 1762; Index Regn. Veg. 117, 1770.

Cedrella Mahag. L., Syst. Nat., ed. 10, 2: 940, 1759.

S. Mahagoni (L.) L., Sp. Pl., ed. 2, 1: 548, 1762.

S. Mahogoni L. ex Lam., Encyc. Méth. Bot. 3: 678–679, (1789) = [1791].

See Little, U. S. Dept. Agric., Handb. 41: 411, 1953.

950. *Suaeda australis* (R. Br.) Moq. var. *nova zelandica* J. B. MacKay & V. J. Chapman, Roy. Soc. N. Z., Trans. 82(1): 42–43, 1954.

S. fruticosa Forsk., Fl. Aegypt.-Arab. 70, 1775.

Salsola fruticosa (L.) Forst. f., Fl. Ins. Austral. Prodr. 21, 1786.

Salsola fruticosa L., Mant. 2: 347, 1771.

951. *Hutchinsia* [R. Br. in] Ait., Hort. Kew., ed. 2, 4: 82, 1812.

Hutschinsia D. Dietr., Syn. Pl. 1: 579, 1839.

Hutchina Wight & Arn. in Wight, Contrib. Bot. Ind. 34, 1834.

Hutchinsia Agardh, Syn. Alg. Scand., xxvi, 53, 1817.

Hutschinsia R. Br. ex Reichenb. in Mössler, Handb. Gewächsk. 2(2): 1,124, 1828.

Hutchintia Bory in Duperr., Voy. La Coquille Crypt. 224, 1828.

952. *Philadelphus triflorus* Wall., Cat. (Num. List Pl. E. Ind.) No. 3,653, 1831.

P. triflorus Wall. ex Royle, Ill. Bot. Him. 1: 215–216, 1835.

P. triflorus Wall. ex Loudon, Arb. Frut. Brit. 2: 955, 1838.

P. triflorus Wall. ex Koch in Wochenschr. Gärtn. Pfl. 2: 228, 1859.

P. nepalensis Koehne, Dendrol. 183, 1893.

See C. Schneider, Ill. Hdb. Laubholzk. 1: 373, 1906.
Hu, Arn. Arb., Jour. 36: 89–90, 1955.

953. *Triticum trachycaulum* Link, Hort. Reg. Bot. Descr. 2: 189, 1833.

Elymus trachycaulus (Link) Gould ined., Rhodora 56: 28, 1954.

T. pauciflorum Schwein. in Keating, Narr. Exped. St.
Peter's River 2: 383, 1824.

Agropyron pauciflorum (Schwein.) Hitchc., Am. Jour. Bot.
21: 132, 1934.

Elymus pauciflorus Lam., Tabl. Encyc. 1: 207, 1791; Poir.
in Lam., Encyc. Méth. Bot. Suppl. 2: 547, (1811) =
[1812].

Agropyrum pauciflorum Schur, Siebenb. Ver. Naturw., Verh.
10: 77, 1859.

954. *Tectaria filix mas* (L.) Cav., Descr. Pl. 251, 1802.

Polypodium filix mas L., Sp. Pl. 1,090, 1753.

Dryopteris filix mas (L.) Schott, Gen. Fil., unnumbered pl.
9, 1834.

Polystichum Felix Mas (L?) Roth, in Roem. Arch. 2(1):
106, 1799.

Aspidium Filix mas (L.) Sw. in Schrad., Jour. 1800(2): 38,
1801.

Nephrodium Filix mas (L.) Rich. in Marthe, Cat. Jard. Méd.
Paris 129, 1801.

Lophodium Filix-mas (L.) Newm., Phytol. 4: app. XX, 1851.

955. *Pandanus ornatus* (Gaud.) Kurz, Roy. Asiat. Soc. Bengal,
Jour. 38(2): 3, 147, 1869.

Fisquetia ornata Gaud., Bot. Voy. La Bonite, Atlas pl. 5,
fig. 1, 8, 9, n. d. =[1841].

P. ornatus Hort., Hort. Soc. London, Jour. Proc. & Misc.
n. s. 1: 1, 1868.

P. Lindenii Warb., Engler's Pflanzenreich IV, 9: 88, 1900.

956. *Pseudotsuga taxifolia* (Lamb.) Britton, New York Acad.
Sci., Trans. 8: 74, 1889.

Pinus taxifolia Lamb., Descr. Genus Pinus 1: 51, pl. 33,
1803.

Pinus taxifolia Salisb., Prodr. Hort. Chapel Allerton 399,
1796.

Abies taxifolia Lamb. ex Poir. in Lam., Encyc. Méth. Bot.
6: 523, (1804) =[1805].

A. taxifolia Mus. ex Du Tour, Nouv. Dict. Hist. Nat. 20:
114, 1803.

A. taxifolia Desf., Tabl. École Bot. Mus. Nat. 206, 1804.

A. Douglasii Hort. ex Loudon var. *taxifolia* Loudon, Arb.
    Frut. Brit. 4: 2,319, fig. 2,231, 1838.

A. Menziesii Mirb., Paris Mus. Hist. Nat., Mém. 13: 63,
    1825.

A. mucronata Raf., Atl. Jour. 1: 120, 1832.

A. Douglasii (Lamb.) Lindl., Penny Cycl. 1: 32, ill. 1833.

Pinus Douglasii Sabine ex D. Don in Lamb., Descr. Genus
    Pinus, ed. 3 (8vo.) 2: unnumbered page following 145,
    pl. [47], 1832.

Pseudotsuga Douglasii (Lindl.) Carr., Traité Gén. Conif.,
    ed. 2, 256, 1867.

Pseudotsuga mucronata (Raf.) Sudw. in Holz., U. S. Natl.
    Herb., Contr. 3: 266, 1895.

Pseudotsuga vancouverensis Flous, Soc. d'Hist. Nat.
    Toulouse, Bul. 66: 340, 1934; Lab. Forest. Toulouse,
    Trav. tome 1, vol. 2, art. 6: 12, ill., 1934.

Pseudotsuga Menziesii (Mirb.) Franco, Soc. Broteriana
    (Coimbra), Bol. II, 24: 74, 1950.

    See Sudworth, U. S. Dept. Agric., Div. Forestry, Bul. 17:
        23–24, 1898;
            Sprague & Greene, Kew Bul. Misc. Inf. 79–80, 1938;
            Little, Am. Jour. Bot. 31: 594–595, 1944;
            Soc. Am. Foresters, Taxon 4: 20, 1955;
            Gleason, Rhodora 57: 332–335, 1955;
            de Wit, Taxon 5: 5, 1956;
            Krajina, Madroño 13: 265–267, 1956.
            Stafleu, Taxon 5: 18–19, 38–39, 1956;
            Ross, Taxon 5: 41–43, 1956;
            Shinners, Taxon 5: 43–46, 1956.

957. *Pritchardia affinis* Beccari var. *Holaphila* Beccari, Bishop
    Mus., Mem. 8(1): 39, 1921.

    P. affinis Beccari var. *halophila* Beccari, Bishop Mus.,
        Mem. 8(1): 2, 10, 12, 19, 23, pl. 4, fig. A, 1921.

958. *Ranunculus Pallash* Schlecht. ex Benson, Am. Midl. Nat.
    53: 255, 1955.

    R. Pallasii Schlecht., Animad. Ranunc. 1: 15, pl. 2, 1819.

INDEX*

*Names of genera and higher taxa are printed flush, those of species are indented once, and those of all subdivisions of species are indented twice. The number listed is the case number.